By James Norman Hall

DOCTOR DOGBODY'S LEG

LOST ISLAND

A WORD FOR HIS SPONSOR
A Narrative Poem

THE FAR LANDS

THE FORGOTTEN ONE
And Other True Tales of the South Seas

In Collaboration with Charles Nordhoff

FALCONS OF FRANCE

MUTINY ON THE BOUNTY

MEN AGAINST THE SEA

PITCAIRN'S ISLAND

THE HURRICANE

THE DARK RIVER

NO MORE GAS

BOTANY BAY

MEN WITHOUT COUNTRY

THE HIGH BARBAREE

The Forgotten One

The Forgotten One

AND OTHER TRUE TALES

OF THE SOUTH SEAS

by James Norman Hall

An Atlantic Monthly Press Book

Little, Brown and Company · Boston

1 9 5 2

ATLANTIC—LITTLE, BROWN BOOKS
ARE PUBLISHED BY
LITTLE, BROWN AND COMPANY
IN ASSOCIATION WITH
THE ATLANTIC MONTHLY PRESS

*Published simultaneously
in Canada by McClelland and Stewart Limited*

PRINTED IN THE UNITED STATES OF AMERICA

TO MY SON
CONRAD

I wish to thank Messrs. Houghton Mifflin Company and the editors of the *Atlantic Monthly* and the *Saturday Evening Post,* for kind permission to collect such of these stories as have previously appeared in print.

Contents

The Forgotten One

I. The Forgotten One

I HAD BEEN READING late that evening. Sitting on my veranda with a shaded lamp on the table beside me, I had entered at once, without effort, into a world revealed so vividly, with such imaginative insight, that although the air my body breathed was heavy with the humid fragrance of tropical vegetation and crickets were chirping in the hibiscus shrubbery close by, I had traveled in spirit as far as Russia and was conscious only of "the clear black sky of the northern winter, decorated with the sumptuous fires of the stars." It will be understood that I returned with difficulty to an awareness of present circumstances. Chancing to glance up from my book I thought for the fraction of a second that I had seen an apparition.

The man, a powerfully built native of middle age, barefoot, dressed in blue denim trousers and a coat of white drill, was standing just outside the circle of lamplight. I had heard no slightest sound, and it had not occurred to him, apparently, to attract my attention by clearing his throat or rapping on one of the veranda posts. I wondered how long he might have been standing thus, quietly waiting for me to notice him. The moment I did so he came forward with the customary Polynesian greeting, "May you live!" He had arrived at Tahiti that afternoon and had walked out from Papeete to bring me a letter which, he said, would explain the reason for this late visit. The white man who had written it had asked him to deliver it as soon as possible. I opened and read it at once:

TANAO, LOW ARCHIPELAGO

DEAR SIR:

The service I am about to ask of you is one that I would hesitate to ask even of an old friend, but you are the only white man I know in this part of the Pacific and I must appeal to you however reluctantly.

I am ill, and as I have grave doubts as to my recovery I must try to put my affairs in order. I have no one with me but an old Chinese servant, Ling Foo, whom you may remember. Could you come to see me? I have chartered a Paumotu cutter for the purpose of carrying this letter, and if you find it possible to come this same cutter will bring you to the island. I realize that you may not be able to leave at once and I have, therefore, instructed the man who brings this letter — he is the owner of the vessel — to await your orders.

Yours very truly
RONALD CRICHTON

The letter had been written by hand, on a sheet of foolscap, but the lines did not follow the ruled spaces. They ran unevenly across the page, meeting, even crossing in some places, widely apart in others. Plainly it had been written by a man so ill that he could scarcely hold the pen. The appearance of the letter quite as much as the message it conveyed convinced me of the urgency of this matter. I asked the man who brought it — his name was Maitua — how he had chanced to call at Tanao. He explained that he and two other men, inhabitants of the island of Hao, had been returning there from Man-

[4]

gareva, an island of the Gambier Group at the southeastern extremity of the Low Archipelago, and had been blown off their course by a southerly gale. After the storm they had passed close by Tanao, and observing a signal fire lighted on the beach, two of them had gone ashore to see what was wanted. An old Chinese waiting there led them to the house of the white man. The *popaa* was very ill and had offered him ten thousand francs if he would sail to Tahiti at once to deliver a letter he would give him.

"What did he tell you to do in case I could not be found?" I asked.

"He said we were to return to Tanao as soon as possible to carry his Chinaman to some island where he might take passage for Tahiti."

"Did he speak of wanting a doctor?"

"No."

"What do you think of his condition? Is it serious?"

"Unless you can come with me at once I doubt that we shall find him living," the man replied.

At one o'clock the following afternoon we were well out at sea, and as soon as we had passed the northeastern extremity of Tahiti the cutter was set on the course of her seven-hundred-mile voyage. There were four of us aboard: Maitua, owner of the cutter, his two companions Nau and Mangi, and myself. The barometer had fallen and the sky looked threatening. The wind was blowing from the westward, more strongly every moment as we came out from the shelter of the island. Westerly and southwesterly winds often mean bad weather in this part of the Pacific, but the month was June and nothing more serious than a moderate gale was to be expected, with frequent heavy squalls of rain. Small though she was, the cutter was an excellent sea boat and I watched with satisfaction as she settled down to her work. It was a fair wind for us.

Three days later it went round to the southeast again, and having blown freshly for several hours died away completely; but by that time we had three hundred miles of the voyage behind us. As the cutter rocked over the long glassy undulations the reef points pattered against the canvas with a sound like the drumming of so many nervous fingers impatient in idleness. Nau and Mangi rigged a mat over the boom and crawled under it to sleep. Presently Maitua joined them; there was no reason for sitting longer at the wheel. The sun set in a sea that reflected perfectly the shapes of a few fleecy clouds. It was what the natives call a *huihui mania,* a great calm. There was nothing to do but wait.

I wondered whether Crichton was waiting as well, or whether we were not already too late. Maitua had told me that the voyage from Tanao had taken eight days. The return voyage might require ten or twelve, what with the calms and head winds we had reason to expect at that time of year. A feeling of desolation came over me as I pictured Crichton dying on that remote atoll with only a taciturn old Chinese servant for company.

Sitting on the wheel box, in the gathering darkness, I went back in thought to the day, in 1920, when I first met him. I had been demobilized from the Army only a few months earlier, and feeling the need for solitude, after the herded life in France, I sailed from San Francisco for an indefinite sojourn in the South Seas. Shortly after arriving at Tahiti I felt a desire to penetrate even farther into the wastes of the Pacific, so I took the first opportunity that presented itself for moving on. This was a small trading schooner, the *Caleb Winship*, bound to the Tuamotu or, as it is more commonly called, the Low, or Dangerous, Archipelago. Crichton chanced to be a passenger on this vessel. He was traveling in company with a dignified, gentle-mannered old Polynesian lady of sixty or thereabout, dressed in a flowered Mother Hubbard, with her white hair hanging in a single braid down her back. He himself was a well-set-up man about six feet tall, with clear blue eyes and reddish-brown hair burned to a lighter hue around the edges by constant exposure to the sun. He was in his middle twenties, so I judged, and had both the appearance and the manners of a cultivated man. I decided at first sight that he was English and wondered in a speculative way what had brought him to this part of the world.

Tino, the half-caste supercargo of the *Winship*, was very curious about Crichton and on our first evening at sea he took me aside to speak of him. Who was he, where did he come from, and what in the name of common sense did he mean to do on that godforsaken circle of reef called Tanao? The island was not worth much, he told me. The land area was small and even if it were all planted to coconut palms in full bearing the output would not amount to ten tons of copra per year. And yet, here was this Englishman, or Swede, or Dane — whatever he was — going out there to settle with the old Kanaka woman who owned the place! He'd taken a five-year lease on it with the option of purchase at the end of that time.

This much Tino had learned from the old woman. Her people had owned Tanao time out of mind, but they were all dead or had gone elsewhere to live. Her husband and two sons had died in the influenza epidemic of 1918, and a third son, the last of her children, had been drowned at sea, while fishing. After this she had lived alone for months until a passing schooner gave her an opportunity to go to Tahiti where she had relatives.

"She stayed there for some time," said Tino; "then it seems the poor old thing got to hankering for home again! It's queer how these natives love their islands. It may be nothing but a sandbank with half a hundred coconut palms and *miki-miki* trees growing on it, a thousand miles from nowhere; but it's home to them. They'll never be happy away from it. She tried to persuade some of her *fetii* — what you call it, relatives — to go back there with her. They said no, of course. Tahiti was home to them and they weren't fools enough to go to a place where there's nothing to eat but coconuts and fish.

"Then, somehow, she met this Crichton, and he jumped at the chance she offered him. The old lady says he's promised to stay, for good. He speaks native, and good native too. I've heard him talkin' with her though he hasn't said yes or no or how-do-you-do to me since he came aboard. He must have been living on Tahiti or somewhere in the Group for a long time. I thought I knew everyone hereabouts, but I never laid eyes on this man till he showed up at the wharf and asked for passage to Tanao. I didn't want to go there; the island's a hundred and fifty miles off my course for this voyage, so I asked him three times the regular passage money. He paid it straight off! Tanao . . . Wait till he sees it! I'll bet you a five-gallon demijohn of the best rum in Papeete that he'll be comin' back with us. He don't know what he's letting himself in for; that's my opinion."

Apparently he did know, however; at any rate he failed to come back with us. We stopped at the island a little more than twenty-four hours, unloading supplies for him. There is no passage into the Tanao lagoon. The reef is dangerous and one of the *Caleb Winship's* surf boats was damaged in making a crossing. Tino was wild about this but I knew nothing of it until later, having gone ashore earlier with Crichton and the old lady. Throughout the day and the night I had the feeling that he was secretly wishing us away and would be heartily glad to see the last of us. Although he treated the old lady with kindness and consideration I felt that he wished her away as well; that he wanted to be entirely alone on the island. What was it, I wondered — a form of selfishness? A desire to be, like Crusoe, monarch of all he surveyed? Or had he perhaps, as Tino suggested, been mixed up in some affair that he was ashamed of, that made it necessary for him to hide away from the sight of other men? But this latter supposition I put aside at once. I knew nothing of his past life, but if his was not a trustworthy face, then I had never seen one. I would have taken oath that he would be incapable of a mean or dishonorable act. Furthermore, no man with a guilty conscience would have gone to a place where he would be so terribly alone with it.

My conclusion, after summing up the little evidence I had to go by, was that solitude was a vital need of his nature; not a temporary need as with most men, but a craving as fundamental as hunger, or thirst, but unlike these in that he had never been able to satisfy it. I gathered from one or two remarks of his that he had long been seeking just such an island as Tanao, and when I asked how long he meant to stay there he said, "Always. All my life," in a quiet assured way that left no doubt in my mind as to the sincerity of his intention. I had never before met anyone who seemed so detached from life, so lacking in dependence upon any sort of companionship, brute or human. Nevertheless, after I had seen the island I doubted that any man could remain content in a place so inconceivably lonely.

We sailed from the island late in the afternoon, having been delayed in getting away because of the damaged reef boat. Tino insisted on pushing off at once, the moment the repairs were completed. Crichton and the old woman were on the lagoon side of the main island at the time so that I had no opportunity to bid them good-by, but as we were getting under way I saw him emerge from the shadows of the palms and stand for a moment, hand shading his eyes, looking out toward the schooner. In that wide land- and seascape his figure looked small and childlike and pathetic. I waved, but evidently he didn't see me, for there was no response. For three hours I sat by the rail, aft, watching the island dwindling and blurring until, at sunset, it was lost to view beneath the rim of the southern horizon. Still I looked back, imagining that I could see a diminishing circle of surf-battered reef and palm-clad islets — a mere speck at last — dropping farther and farther away down the reverse slope of the sea, as though it were vanishing for all time from the knowledge and the concern of men.

Four years passed. Meanwhile, like many another ex-soldier, I had been wandering here and there, looking on at life in a rapidly changing world. I seemed to have lost the faculty for living in a settled, purposeful way. After two years of voyaging from island to island in the Pacific, I returned to the United States where I continued my nomadic existence, camping in hotels and in the guest bedrooms in the houses of old friends, but never staying long in any one place. In the summer of 1922 I went to Iceland and spent the following winter there, traveling on horseback through that beautiful, sparsely populated country, gazing at the northern lights from vantage points on or near the Arctic Circle. I went to the Faroe Islands and from there to Norway and elsewhere in Europe; then home again, via New York, and on westward to the Pacific Coast across the prairies and plains, and the vast deserts of Arizona and New Mexico.

Crichton was often in my thoughts during this prolonged interval of wandering. I could not account for the deepness of the impression he had made upon me in the course of our voyage in the *Caleb Winship*. To be sure, we had been thrown much together during that voyage, but our companionship had rested upon very slight foundations. He seemed to be afraid of any relationship even remotely approaching intimacy, and gave me the impression of being perpetually upon his guard. At times it struck me that he was merely shy, even morbidly so; therefore I was careful not to intrude upon him in any way. As a result I knew nothing of his serious thoughts and interests, nor he anything of mine. Only once did we have what might be called a conversation. In reply to a chance remark he spoke with animation of various aspects of native life. It was plain that he had a wide knowledge of the history and folk lore of that branch of the Polynesian family and of the various dialects spoken amongst the islands of the eastern Pacific. I was a willing listener, but not for long. Of a sudden he broke off, as though he felt that he had been guilty of an impropriety, and for the rest of the day he scarcely spoke.

Despite the briefness of the first visit I must have left a part of myself at Tanao, as it is said one does wherever one goes. However this may be, certain it is that, ever since I had left the island, in the strangest circumstances and at the most unlikely moments a picture of the place would float into consciousness and I would see the coconut palms of Tanao bending to the southeast wind, and Crichton sitting in the shade at the upper slope of the beach, his hands clasped around his knees, looking out over the empty sea. In Iceland, while watching the visible music of the northern lights, I had felt the softness of the air at Tanao, and the smoke of the surf on my face from the combers rising to their height and thundering over the reef. I would hear the old woman — Mama Ruau (Grandma), he called her — singing softly to herself as she broiled fish over a fire of coconut shells on the lagoon beach. The island and its two lonely inhabitants were more real to me at times than the streets through which I passed or the people with whom I sat at table, but it was Crichton who was oftenest in my thoughts. I wondered about him, and for some reason was disturbed about him. It was an unusual thing for a young man to bury himself as he had done. Even for an authentic lover of solitude such a procedure seemed to me more than a little dangerous. However I took comfort in the thought that he himself must have realized this long since and have gone elsewhere.

I returned to Tahiti in 1924, having decided to make my home there in the future, and again took quarters at the Aina Paré, a ramshackle hotel on the Papeete waterfront.

I might have left the place only the week before. There was the same old paper on the wooden walls; the same mosquito netting around the bed, the rents in it neatly drawn together; the same tin bucket with the dent in it by the washstand; the same dilapidated wardrobe, the doors slightly askew and the shelves covered with pages from the *Sydney Bulletin* and the *Auckland Weekly News,* and the same portly, barefoot landlord, dressed only in a waistcloth, coming up for a chat while I drank my morning coffee. We had a pleasant talk about island affairs, and in the midst of it I chanced to speak of a hole in the floor of the veranda, and how I had nearly broken my leg there, coming in in the dark the night before.

"Why, don't you remember that hole?" he asked, quite seriously, with genuine surprise, and I realized that the fault was not his for not having it repaired, but mine for not having remembered during the four years that repair was needed. It was good to be back in a place where life was as leisurely as that; where all things, animate and inanimate, even a hole in a veranda floor, seemed to partake of a timeless ideal existence like that of the figures on Keats's Grecian urn.

It was still quite early. Chinese were sweeping the street with their long-handled brooms, heaping into neat piles the dead twigs and leaves and withered blossoms from the flamboyant trees, against the coming of the rubbish cart. I well remembered the former driver of this cart, Girot, a thin, wiry little Frenchman of uncertain age said to have been the son of a former convict from New Caledonia. He called his horse "Banane," and carried on with her a continuous animated conversation as they wandered along the street, Girot pausing at times to listen to her replies audible only to himself. Were they too, I wondered, under the enchantment of timelessness? Yes, here they came, presently, Girot barefoot as usual, carrying the two little boards with which he scooped up the piles of leaves. He was in the usual costume: floppy pandanus hat with the hole in the crown, tattered undershirt, and denim trousers faded to a whitish blue by many washings. Banane was a trifle bonier, if possible, than I had remembered her. She moved as deliberately as ever, but Girot was reproaching her in the old manner for going too fast.

"Whoa! Whoa, sacré nom de Balzac! Écoute, Banane! Penses-tu que nous sommes sur un champ de course? . . . Comment? . . . Ah, non, alors! Oui, je comprends: pour toi ça ne fait rien. Mais pour moi? Je ne suis pas garçon, moi. J'ai plus de soixante ans. Maintenant nous allons jusqu'au coin de la rue — tu vois? Là! Et la prochaine fois quand je dis 'Whoa!' arrête-toi! Tu comprends? . . . Bon! . . . Allez! En route!"

No one paid the least attention to them and at last they were out of hearing. Natives were passing to and from the market place with strings of fish, baskets of fresh-water shrimps, fruit and vegetables. It was good to hear again their laughter, their soft voices; to smell the humid fragrance of tropical vegetation; to look across the lagoon and sea to the island of Moorea, every mountain peak outlined clearly against the sky — all that a South Sea island should be and surpassing my most splendid dreams of one, as a boy. I drank my coffee slowly, watching the animated scene in the street below; then I set out for a stroll along the waterfront.

Vessels from all parts of the eastern Pacific were moored along the sea wall, unloading pearl shell and copra, taking in cargoes of rice and flour and sugar, tinned food and assorted merchandise. Among them was the *Caleb Winship*, her rail festooned with bunches of green bananas and baskets of oranges and mangoes, evidence that she was about to sail for the Low Islands. Tino, her former supercargo, had since been made captain. I found him in the cabin checking over bills of lading.

"Well!" he said, glancing up and holding out his hand, sidewise. "Haven't seen you for some time. Where you been keeping yourself, out in the country?"

I told him I had just returned from the U.S.A.; then, after a brief chat of different matters, I asked in a by-the-way fashion for news of Crichton.

"Crichton? . . . Crichton? Who's — Oh! You mean that Swede, that Dane . . ."

"He is an Englishman," I said.

"Whatever he was. Hell, no! I ain't seen him since the time we was out there; when the whaleboat was stove in crossin' the reef. He might be dead for all I know — or care, for that matter."

It was plain that Tino was still sore on the subject of Crichton. His reason in consenting to carry him to Tanao was that he thought he had plans of commercial interest in view. When he had satisfied himself that the island was as poor as it had always been he set Crichton down as crazy or some knave in hiding. Remembering his disgust at the loss of time in going so far out of his way I knew it would be useless asking him to call there again. Nevertheless, I did ask, for the *Winship* was bound in that general direction.

"Tanao? Not much! I'm not traveling for my health. What do you want to go back there for, if it's any of my business?"

"I liked the place," I said. "You don't find such islands in my part of the world."

"Ought to be glad you don't. Why anyone should go to one of them godforsaken holes of his own free will beats me. Well,

that Swede can rot in his. I expect he has. He's probably dead
or gone somewheres else long before this."

I loafed through long afternoons on the veranda of the
Bougainville Club and other favorite resorts of traders, planters, pearl buyers and sailors, making an occasional discreet inquiry about Crichton, for I remembered how jealous with
respect to his retreat he had been. He had seemed almost
afraid to mention the island by name, as though to do so in
the presence of others might sully for him the purity of its
loneliness. The island being one of the undoubted ends of the
earth, I was not very successful in my quest for information. "Tanao? Oh, yes," one trader remarked. "The *Madeleine*
went on the reef there — let me see, when was it? Nineteen-
four, I think." This was about as recent a bit of news as I
gathered in talk on the Club veranda. As for Crichton no one,
apparently, in that place where everyone is known, could tell
me what had become of him.

Then I met an old friend, Chan Lee, owner of the schooner
Toafa. I had once made a long voyage with Chan. He has all
the fine personal qualities of the Oriental at his best, but he
carries minding-his-own-business to odd lengths. It was not
until some time after I had spoken to him of Crichton that he
admitted knowing him.

"Go Tanao once year," he said, holding up a finger as
though to emphasize the infrequency of his visits. "Not much
copla — five ton."

He told me that he had passed the atoll in 1920 — it must
have been only a month or two after my visit — and had sent
his ship's boat ashore for a supply of firewood for the galley
stove. He had not known there was anyone living on the
island. Crichton came out to the schooner and arranged

with Chan to call once yearly to bring him supplies. On the first visit made under this arrangement he had carried out a schooner load of books and household furnishings that had arrived for Crichton from England. All of this had to be taken over the reef in the ship's boat. It was a long and difficult business, but Crichton had paid him well for it.

"Clichton vely rich man," said Chan. Then, as an afterthought, apparently, he added: "He say, suppose I see you, tell you come back, some time."

I was both surprised and pleased by this information. Slightly as I knew Crichton I had a genuine liking for him but I had no reason to believe that my regard was reciprocated. His attitude toward me on the *Caleb Winship* was, as I have said, courteous but extremely reserved.

"Yes, he say that," Chan added. "Bimeby nex week I go. You comealong me?"

During the voyage with Chan I became convinced, intuitively, that Crichton's destiny was, or would be, a tragic one; that he was, somehow, doomed. I considered his situation from every point of view; took myself in hand, so to speak, as though trying to persuade another person of the absurdity of this apprehension. What was there to be concerned about? What ground had I for supposing there was anything amiss with Crichton? Here was a young Englishman of cultivated tastes, evidently of good family, who happened to be nongregarious, and who for this reason chose to live on a small coral island in the middle of the Pacific. Was there, necessarily, anything strange or unnatural or even dangerous in that? Other men of similar tastes had lived shut off from the world and had found happiness in doing so. Why not this one? Self-confidence in such a man was usually based upon self-knowledge. This was not the case of a man foolishly enamored of a way of life for which he was unfitted. He had chosen it because he loved it and was conscious of resources within himself to make solitude not only endurable but pleasant. The fact that he was still living on Tanao was proof enough, surely, that he had not been mistaken in his choice.

So I tried to reason myself out of my misgivings; meanwhile, the *Toafa* proceeded on her way. Chan had a dozen islands to visit before calling at Tanao and during the early part of the voyage the schooner was crowded with native passengers. These were gradually dispersed, the last of them at an island one hundred miles from Tanao. We were three days in covering the last leg of the voyage, and thirty-eight days out from Papeete when we sighted the island.

Crichton need never have feared for the purity of its loneliness. It was lonelier than the sea. It seemed to have gathered to itself an esoteric kind of loneliness, peculiar to the man who lived at the heart of it. It seemed a place he had dreamed into being, created out of fancy through sheer strength of longing. And there he was, alone of his kind, and there he had been during four years, without once having left it. Chan gave me this information.

I asked whether he had taken a native wife.

"No, no womans," said Chan. "I want get him nice Paumotu wife. Help make copla; make him plenty childrens. He no want."

He had, however, provided Crichton with an old Chinese to act as cook and to care for his house. There was no one else except Mama Ruau from whom he had leased the island. She was still living, in good health; at least she had been a year ago.

"What about letters," I asked; "and books, and papers? Does he receive many?"

Chan showed me the mail he was carrying out to Crichton. There was some printed matter, book catalogues and the like, and only one letter, as impersonal in appearance as a bank note. In fact, the name and address of a London Trust Company was stamped on the envelope.

At this second approach to his island a truer conception of Crichton's isolation came home to me. He was like those men Matthew Arnold speaks of in "Rugby Chapel": men who vanish without leaving a trace behind them:

> . . . and no one asks
> Who or what they have been,
> More than he asks what waves,
> In the moonlit solitudes mild
> Of the midmost Ocean, have swell'd,
> Foam'd for a moment, and gone.

Certainly, that seemed to be true of Crichton, and he was still living, in the vigor of early manhood. But, beyond the limits of his island he had long been as good as dead and buried. He had never mentioned family or friends.

To continue, as we drew near the atoll I climbed to the main cross trees for a wider view. We passed the northeast extremity of the island close inshore, between three and four in the afternoon. At that point one sees little more than barren reef washed over by the surf. There is one islet on the reef, a small boy's dream of an island to be shipwrecked on;

indeed, the bones of an old vessel still lie there, high and dry beyond the reef and bleached white by the sun — all that remains from the wreck of the *Madeleine*. The islet is just boy size, not more than one hundred paces across, either way. It is of clean coral sand, as level as a floor with clumps of green bush scattered over it. Eight tall coconut palms grow there, four in one clump and three in another, with one tree standing apart, holding its cluster of fronds over the surface of the lagoon. At one end of the islet the reef is pierced by a zigzag strip of blue water but the passage is too narrow to permit entrance to any craft larger than a skiff or canoe. On that side an old *puketea* tree throws a patch of deep shade on the sand. Within the shelter of it was a thatch-roofed hut open on all sides, and I saw a rough-hewn bench facing seaward with its back against the tree.

"Very likely Crichton comes here to fish," I thought, but the place was deserted now. The sunlight, of that mellow, golden quality of late afternoon, gilded the stems of the palms. Nothing moved save the trees bending to the wind and their shadows on the coral sand.

We passed the islet all too quickly, then stood away to come in to the main island on the other tack. Tanao is elliptical in shape, eight miles long and five broad, with seven widely separated islets along the circle of reef and one small *motu* in the lagoon near the main island where Crichton lived. This last is the only piece of land of any consequence, sickle-shaped, about half a mile in length and from three to four hundred paces across in the widest part. The central portion was well planted to coconut palms, but toward the ends where it narrowed to the reef, nothing grew but low scrub. From my perch aloft I could look across to the islets on the far side of the lagoon, where the trees appeared to be growing directly out of the sea.

With my binoculars I searched the shore line for some time before I saw Crichton. He and the old woman were sitting within the border of shade at the upper slope of the beach, their figures hidden momentarily by the sunlight-filtered smoke of the surf. He was dressed in shorts and a soft-brimmed native hat. Mama Ruau was in her best black dress and hat. She pointed toward the schooner from time to time; then I saw her take Crichton by the shoulders, as though he had been an unobservant child, and turn him till he sat directly facing us.

There was a heavy onshore swell, and the roar of the surf came to us over the water with a gentle, soothing sound, but it increased in volume as we approached. The schooner was brought to, the reef boat lowered, and we approached the shore with four sailors at the oars and one at the steering sweep. The swells seemed ominously high as they swept forward and toppled in a smother of foam and spray over the ledge of the reef. We waited several minutes for a favorable opportunity to cross the reef, the men backing on their oars and the boat steerer standing with his head turned over his shoulder, watching the following seas. Of a sudden he shouted a command; the sailors put their backs into it and we were carried across at dizzy speed. The boat shot down the broad slope of broken water and through the shallows, grounding almost at the spot where Crichton and the old woman were waiting.

"Is it you, Chan?" Crichton called, in native, when he heard the keel bumping and grating over the coral.

"Yes, yes!" the old woman cried. "Don't you believe me?

It is Chan and the *popaa* who first came here with you! *Ia ora na orua!*"

She came forward and took both my hands in hers, searching my face feature by feature.

"*Ua tae mai oé?*" (You have come?) she added, as though still in doubt that anyone from the outside world could reach that lonely place. She had aged considerably in four years, but Crichton had not changed, outwardly, at least. The ghost of the smile I remembered curved his lips almost imperceptibly as he greeted me. His eyes I could not see; they were concealed by dark glasses.

"I am sorry not to have recognized you," he said. "I've had trouble with my eyes due to the glare of the sun but it's nothing serious. Shall we go to the house?"

I remembered the island as I had first seen it — a wilderness of brush, pandanus trees and self-sown coconut palms. Now everything was clean and orderly, the palms thinned out to six or eight paces apart, so that one had views in every direction. A well-shaded road bordered with shrubbery led from the ocean beach to the lagoon. We followed it in silence. Having greeted me he seemed to have nothing more to say. I was again conscious of the feeling of restraint I had felt in his company aboard the *Caleb Winship*. Mama Ruau had gone on ahead; Chan remained at the beach to oversee the landing of some supplies.

At last, with something of an effort I remarked: "You've not been idle here."

"No, there's been enough to do. I found that I needed some help at first. I had Chan bring me a dozen natives from another island. They stayed three months, clearing the land; and they helped build my house."

I had often tried to picture the house he would have. I was not prepared to find so spacious a dwelling. It stood on the lagoon beach at the end of the road, and was in the semi-native style. The roof, of pandanus-leaf thatch, was steeply pitched and extended low over a broad veranda that ran the full length of the house. Crichton halted at the foot of the steps, and for a moment stared at the ground as though deep in thought. He seemed to have forgotten me. Then he said: "I'm sorry. I must go back to the beach. Please make yourself comfortable. You might look over my house if you care to."

A clock with a ship's-bell attachment, striking five as I entered the veranda, demanded immediate attention. "Odd," I thought, "having a clock here." But it would be a wise precaution, perhaps, in so lonely a place. One would need to live by schedule, fill one's days with self-imposed duties to be regularly performed. No doubt Crichton did. The house gave evidence of all but meticulous concern for order, and of the methodical habits of his literal-minded Chinese. Settees, tables and easy chairs were as carefully arranged as the pieces in an upholsterer's display window. The floors, oiled and polished, shone with a dull luster and the straw mats were precisely placed. Four shelves of books ran the length of the inner wall of the veranda. A brief examination revealed that they had been classified and subclassified. Novelists, historians, poets, biographers, travelers stood together and in the ranks of their contemporaries. I estimated that he had at least fifteen hundred volumes in his library, nothing very recent but all of them books to live with. The margins of the pages of a few that I opened were covered with penciled notes and comments and I could see what pleasure and solace Crichton found in their companionship. One section of his library contained books on Polynesia; everything important, it seemed, that had been written about the islands of the eastern Pacific. There were a number of philological books in this section and I remembered the interest Crichton had taken in the study of the various island dialects, speculating, with this study as a basis, on the probable sea routes followed during the early Polynesian migrations.

On a top shelf bare of books were models of ancient sailing canoes, spears and war clubs of ironwood, polished coconut shells and wooden bowls carved with intricate designs; stone axes, adzes, and taro mashers. The windward end of the veranda was enclosed with a wall of plaited palm fronds, built in sections to prop open in fine weather. Crichton's desk stood here, facing a delightful view across an inlet from the lagoon bordered with palms through which, now, a greenish golden sunset light sifted like impalpable dust. A passageway led through the house to a second veranda on the lagoon side. Open doors revealed spacious airy rooms, attractively furnished with sofas, tables, bookshelves and easy chairs.

Returning to the front veranda I walked up and down for some time, thinking, "What a beautiful spot! What an ideal home!" but conscious all the while of a feeling very like depression. I was at a loss to account for this unless it were the clock ticking away with self-important industry as though it were the only one in existence. Within half an hour I revised my opinion as to the wisdom of having a clock. The silence was too profound for any such noisy piece of furniture. I could all but hear the steady drip, drip of the minutes and the tiny splash they made as they fell into the sea of time past. Then I found myself listening for voices . . . of the wife who should have been there; of Crichton's unborn children. It was that kind of house: too large, it seemed to me, for one man, and too homelike for spiritual comfort under those circumstances. One would have thought that Crichton had built it for the very purpose of evoking ghostly presences; to shelter some ideal conception of a family which he preferred to the warm, living, imperfect reality. Or, perhaps, not satisfied with the superficial aspects of a solitude that would have daunted most men, he meant his house to accentuate it, to remind him of its inviolability. Certainly he had succeeded in building into it a personality as strange as his own. It seemed conscious of having been prepared for others beside its lonely tenant, and to be awaiting them with the complaisant assurance that they would never come.

I too waited — anything but complaisantly, for the return of my host, reproaching myself, now that it was too late, for having taken a welcome for granted. To be sure, I had been invited, according to Chan, but that was three years earlier and I had neglected to ask whether Crichton had ever again inquired about me. An hour passed and still I waited, sitting on the top step of the veranda, as Crichton must have done times without number at that hour, looking down his empty roadway to the empty sea. The sun had set and the colorless light faded swiftly from the sky. The fronds of the palms, swaying gently in the last faint tremors of the breeze, came gradually to rest. In the trancelike calm of earth and air I was conscious again of the beating of the surf on the reef. Now it was measured, regular, as though it were the pulsing of blood through the mighty heart of Solitude. Now it seemed the confused roar of street traffic from a thousand cities, mingled with the voices of all humankind, flowing smoothly, in soundless waves, in narrowing circles, over the rim of the world, to break audibly at last on this minute ringed shoal in the farthermost sea of Silence.

After listening to that lonely sound for at least another half hour I began to feel decidedly uncomfortable. Dusk deepened into night and still I waited. At last I saw a glimmer of light along the passageway leading through the house, and presently a dinner gong was sounded — one of those old-fashioned bronze gongs whose soft musical summons faintly stirred innumerable ghostly recollections. I was hungry, and supposing that Crichton had returned another way and was waiting for me, I went along the passage in search of him.

I have but mentioned thus far the veranda on the lagoon side of the house. It was semicircular in shape, extending over shoal water to the brink of a magnificent coral precipice. Standing at the edge of it one looks down into a submarine garden of exquisite beauty. Gorgeously colored fish of the most fantastic shapes swim lazily in and out of the caves which honeycomb the precipice, and from the floor of the lagoon rise forests of coral, spreading their delicate branches into water as clear as air.

Emerging from the passageway I gave an inward gasp of wonder at the beauty and strangeness of the scene before me. It was now deep night. The veranda lay open to the sky, and the reflections of the stars in the water were so bright and clear it was easy to imagine that the house was adrift, motionless, in space. But what first attracted my attention was a small table, laid for one, and holding a shaded lamp. Standing near it was a Chinese with a napkin over his arm — a man so small and wrinkled and gnomelike that he might have stepped out of some centuries-old book of Chinese fairy tales. But he was dressed in a cotton shirt and a black *pareu,* or waistcloth, reaching to his ankles. Standing with his back to the starlit lagoon he made a striking and memorable picture. His large bald head gleamed softly, as though it had been polished with coconut oil; the lamplight filled the caverns of his eyes with shadow, and the black waistcloth blended so perfectly with the surrounding darkness that he seemed to be only half a Chinese suspended motionless above two bare feet.

I said "Good evening," but he merely looked at me with a contemplative, detached expression as one might gaze at a rock or tree while thinking of something else. He drew back the single chair at the table, waiting for me to be seated. Glancing over my shoulder a few seconds later I found that he had vanished, as I more than half expected him to do even as I looked at him. He reappeared as noiselessly as he had gone and set a plate of soup before me. It was then that I discovered a piece of folded note paper tucked under the edge of my plate. Wondering what it could be I opened it and read:

I am sorry that I can't join you at dinner, and as the *Toafa* will sail early tomorrow morning it may be that I shall not see you again before you leave. Ling Foo will look after you. Please believe that you are welcome here, and feel free to use my house as though it were your own.

Ling Foo had gone to the kitchen while I was puzzling over this message; at any rate, when I looked up again he was standing at my elbow holding a covered dish which, certainly, he had not been holding a moment before. I would not have been surprised, after he set it down in front of me, to have seen him conjure it away again with his napkin. It required an effort of the imagination to think of that wraith

[27]

of a man who moved as soundlessly as a shadow concerning himself in the usual manner with anything as substantial as food. He brought me an excellent dinner, out of tins to be sure but admirably prepared, and he took away the scarcely tasted dishes as though he had quite expected this. Having placed a lighted lamp on the front veranda and another in the room where I was to sleep he again vanished, this time for good.

I was as forlorn as it is possible for a man to be: a guest in a house where I knew that I was not wanted. "Please believe that you are welcome here" — the words kept repeating themselves in my mind. I tried to believe it, but under the circumstances nothing seemed less likely than that Crichton meant me to accept this absentee welcome in good faith. Common sense should have warned me that a man who had chosen one of the loneliest islands in the Pacific as a home had not done so because he craved companionship. Nevertheless, putting my necessarily unannounced visit in the least favorable light, I felt that he was lacking in consideration to abandon me as he had, in his own house. I had remained ashore at his invitation, and the obligations of hospitality demanded, at the least, that he should not shame me. It would have been easy for him to have pleaded illness. Almost any excuse would have been better than no excuse.

I would have been glad to return to the *Toafa*, but that was impossible. When I had last seen the ship, just after sunset, she was at least three miles offshore and going farther. She had no engines and Chan Lee would stand well out to sea during the night. I smiled, lugubriously however, at thought of my anxiety to leave an island I had dreamed of so often during four years, but those dreams had been concerned with the Crichton I knew, or thought I knew, on board the *Caleb Winship*. Now, going back in detail over the events of my first voyage to his island, I realized how meager my knowledge of him really was. Although we were thrown constantly together, our companionship had been a strangely silent one. Often for days at a time we scarcely spoke. I was new to the islands then and under the spell of my first voyage in the South Seas; it was hard to believe that I was still in the world of reality. Crichton too, I felt, was under the same enchantment. Once, breaking a long silence, he said: "I wish I had come out here years ago. They appeal to the imagination, don't you think — all these islands?" That struck me as a happy expression of one's feeling about them, for we were then in the very heart of the archipelago, with islands all around us, and yet they did not seem real. The glimpses I had into his mind were all of this fragmentary nature and as brief as they were rare. I had taken the rest of him for granted. Even though I were justified, then, in doing so, who could say what might have happened to him in the meantime — what changes might have taken place during four years of complete isolation? Perhaps it had made unbearable to him the prospect of a renewed contact, however slight, with anyone from the outside world. It might even have unbalanced his mind. I was not hopeful as I thought of this. One might love solitude at a distance and long to know it intimately; but the heart of it was too vast, surely, for one poor human waif to snuggle against with impunity, or to attempt to explore in search of the secret of its peace. I tried to put myself in Crichton's place, and succeeded so well — or so ill; I could not be sure which it was — that I came back with a feeling of great relief to my proper identity; but as a result of the attempt I could understand how one might so completely lose touch with human-kind that the mere thought of renewing it, even for a day, would be unendurable.

It was not yet nine o'clock; too early for bed. I returned to the front veranda where I examined at leisure some charts and sketches — Crichton's own handiwork, evidently — which hung on the wall above the bookshelves. There was a detailed, carefully drawn plan of the atoll and another of the main island where his house stood. Some of the sketches were extremely interesting. One had for title: "When the Seas Go Dry." It was a sketch in crayon of a number of the atolls of the Low Archipelago as they would appear from the ocean floor if the waters should recede. Immensely high mountains in the shape of truncated cones were shown, with walls falling almost sheer from a great height to the level of the surrounding country. It was a vividly imaginative impression and true to fact at the same time. One could see that the idea had been suggested by a chart of the archipelago, with its data of soundings, which hung nearby. Another sketch showed Tanao alone, with two pygmy figures standing in the valley below — as they do in old engravings of mountain scenery — one of them pointing to the cliffs towering above them.

Having examined the drawings I turned again to the library, taking volumes at random from the shelves and reading a page here and there. It had been Crichton's practice, apparently, upon acquiring a book, to write on the flyleaf the date and place of reading it. Nearly all of those I looked into had notations of this kind, covering a period of years reaching back to his early youth. He was also fond of marking passages in his books. One of these was in a volume of Shelley's *Lyrics and Minor Poems* which fell open of itself at the Preface to

"Alastor: or The Spirit of Solitude." There was no marginal comment on the page, but the passage underscored was this:

> Among those who attempt to exist without human sympathy, the pure and tender hearted perish through the intensity and passion of their search after its communities, when the vacancy of their spirit suddenly makes itself felt. All else, selfish, blind, and torpid, are those unforeseeing multitudes who constitute, together with their own, the lasting misery and loneliness of the world. Those who love not their fellow beings live unfruitful lives and prepare for their old age a miserable grave.

Under the circumstances the whole of the Preface had a special interest for me and the poem as well, which I had not reread since college days. Drawing my chair close to the lamp I began, and at the second stanza started reading aloud, partly for the companionship of my own voice, and partly that I might better sense the sonorous beauty of the words:

Mother of this unfathomable world,
Favour my solemn song! For I have loved
Thee ever and thee only; I have watched
Thy shadow and the darkness of thy steps,
And my heart ever gazes on the depth
Of thy deep mysteries. I have made my bed
In charnels and on coffins, where black Death
Keeps record of the trophies won from thee;
Hoping to still these obstinate questionings
Of thee and thine, by forcing some lone ghost,
Thy messenger, to render up the tale
Of what we are. In lone and silent hours,
When night makes a weird sound of its own stillness . . .

I had been reading for a quarter of an hour, I should say, sometimes aloud, sometimes silently, when I heard from the adjoining room a slight but very distinct noise: a drumming of fingers against the wall just back of my head. I had never been so curiously startled in my life, before. A cry, a crash of breaking glass, a pistol fired behind my back, might have produced a more violent shock but nothing like such an eerie one. I got up at once, turned down the light, tiptoed into my room at the other end of the veranda and closed the door. The reaction was purely instinctive, as a child's would be upon hearing at night a sound it could not understand. Theoretically, I should then have jumped into bed and hidden under the coverlet, but instinct did not carry me that far. I knew of course that Crichton was in that other room. At least I knew it after hearing the noise. Previous to that the possibility of his presence in the house had not occurred to me. The fact of his sending me a message had given me a sense of his remoteness. I had taken it for granted that he was elsewhere — across the lagoon, perhaps, on one of the other islets; anywhere but under his own roof.

For some time I stood listening, in the middle of the floor; then, hearing no further sound I sat in the darkness by the open window and gave myself up to the most disquieting reflections. I winced at the thought of having read aloud. Had I set to work deliberately to torment Crichton, I doubted whether I could have hit upon a better means for doing so. Deprived, temporarily at least through his sun blindness, of the enjoyment of reading, I had reminded him of the seriousness of the deprivation. Accustomed during four years to all but unbroken silence, he had been compelled to listen to the monotonous intonation of my voice. "Alastor" might very well be the last poem in the world so lonely a man would care to hear read; and he must have heard every word distinctly, for only a thin board partition separated the veranda from the rooms behind it. At last, irritated beyond endurance, he had let me know of his presence.

I was tempted to go to Crichton's room, to apologize for having disturbed him, for having come to Tanao at all. On second thought I decided that I had been sufficiently meddlesome and it seemed best to remain where I was, wearing out the rest of the night as unobtrusively as possible.

But although Ling Foo had garnished and freshened the room and turned the coverlet back, I did not go to bed. Instead, I sat by the window listening to the clock on the veranda measuring eternity. I dozed off at last, to be wakened out of uneasy slumber by the crowing of a cock. It was a welcome sound for I thought day was at hand but this was far from being the case. Low Island fowls, like the islanders themselves, are semi-nocturnal in their habits. Cocks greet the rising of the moon as well as the sun, and often break into a prolonged ecstasy of crowing for no reason at all, in the middle of a starlit night. One can scarcely blame them, for the nights are enchantingly beautiful; but the sound of persistent crowing may be extremely annoying if close at hand, and this cock was perched in some shrubbery just in front of the veranda. A late moon was rising which may have caused the outburst. However that may be he kept it up. With a premonitory flapping of wings he shattered the silence time after time, waiting with seeming intent for it to heal that he might shatter it again, more effectively. The thing got on my nerves; I thought he would never leave off. At last I got up, again tiptoed across the veranda and down the steps, and walked along the lagoon beach, keeping within the shadows of the trees.

The crowing stopped at once. I was in the mood to be chagrined at this, and to take as an intentional affront the habitual action of hermit crabs — there were thousands of them along the beach — snapping into their shells at my approach and closing their doors behind them. The land crabs, too, showed hostility in their own fashion, holding up their little claws in menace, scurrying away on either side and dodging into their holes as though fleeing a pestilence. "I'm having a strange welcome all round," I thought. But Mama Ruau, the old native woman, had been friendly. I had no doubt of the sincerity of her welcome.

Her little thatched hut on the lagoon beach a short distance from Crichton's place seemed as essential a feature of the landscape as the old *kahaia* tree that shaded it. All was silent there. A fire of coconut husks smoldered on the earthen floor of the kitchen at the back. Passing this I knocked on the door post of the dwelling house, and receiving no response looked in. The reflections from the moonlit water made the room almost as light as day. A wooden chest for clothing stood against one wall and a sewing machine in a corner. This was all the furniture the room contained except for a mat spread over the coral sand and some beautifully formed branches of antler coral hanging from the wall posts. The old woman lay on the mat, her hands, palm to palm, tucked under her cheek. She was sleeping so peacefully that I hadn't the heart to waken her but slipped quietly away and sat for a time on the beach nearby.

Here Mama Ruau had prepared supper for Crichton and me on the day of our arrival at the island. I recalled a story that she had told us that evening, which Crichton translated for me: a weird tale of the spirit of the last of her sons who had, somehow, been drowned while spearing fish on the outer reef of a neighboring islet. It appeared to her but rarely, she said, and always in the form of a huge dog. She would see it only at the full of the moon, lying on the lagoon beach, its head resting on its paws. As she approached it would rise to its feet, yawn, stretch, and gaze mournfully at her. Then it would take a long drink of salt water and start at a lope down the beach. Soon it would break into a run, gathering tremendous speed, and upon reaching the end of the islet it would make a flying spring. She would last see it clearly outlined against the moonlit sky, crossing in one gigantic leap the two-mile gap to the islet where her son had been drowned.

The story had made a deep impression upon me, and the simplicity and earnestness of her manner in telling it convinced me of the realness of the apparition to Mama Ruau. She believed in all sorts of spirits, good and bad. Her grandmother, a Marquesan, although converted to Christianity, had never been quite sure what to believe, and shortly before her death at Tanao, many years ago, she had left instructions that a small stone idol which she had always kept was to be set at the head of her grave, and a slab of coral with a cross cut upon it, at the foot. I had seen this grave at the time of my former visit; it is in the family burying ground at the east end of the main islet. As day was long distant I decided to go there again and look at it by moonlight.

I doubt whether there is a cemetery in all the Pacific — except at the bottom of it — more impressively lonely than the one at Tanao. It lies close to the ocean beach where, owing to the contour of the fringing reef, the sea breaks with unusual violence; and the moonlight-silvered spray drifting slowly across the land makes one think of an endless procession of ghosts. There are fifteen or twenty graves in all, most of them in a sadly neglected condition, overgrown with shrubs and coarse vines. I found the grandmother's grave. The little idol, hands folded across its fat paunch, seemed to be gazing with stony-eyed hostility at the nearby cross. An inscription had once been chiseled on the coral slab beneath the cross, but the action of wind and rain had long since made it illegible.

But what interested me more than this grave was another close by, freshly prepared and ready for occupancy. It had been dug to a depth of five or six feet and roofed over with sheets of corrugated iron to keep out the rain. A shallow drainage trench surrounded it and nearby were a number of thin coral slabs chiseled square and the edges beveled with which to cover the grave at last. The headstone was ready to be set in place and on it was cut Mama Ruau's name — Fainau a Hiva. I was not greatly surprised at this, for it is not unusual for Polynesians to make preparations for their end when they know that it cannot be far distant. They have no dread of death; indeed, in old age they seem rather to welcome its approach and make all ready for their last long sleep. Mama Ruau was merely following the custom of her people, but she was too frail, I knew, to have done this work herself. Crichton must have helped her with it, and it struck me that he may have found zest in it as though he were thinking: "It won't be long, now. I'll soon have the island to myself."

I stood for a time, watching the great seventh waves crashing over the reef. The ground trembled under their ceaseless impact and the roar of broken water was loud enough, one would think, to disturb even the repose of the dead. Crichton would be lying here eventually if he held firm to his voluntary exile; but in the ordinary course of events that would be years hence. Meanwhile, what of the present and the years just ahead? Walking slowly back along the outer beach I tried to persuade myself that it was my duty to urge him to come away with us. The trouble he was having with his eyes gave me an excellent pretext. I could suggest the need for his coming to Tahiti for advice and treatment lest his sight be seriously impaired.

Quickening my pace I crossed to the lagoon beach, and as I approached the house that cock started crowing again as though it had been waiting all this while to warn Crichton of the return of his unwelcome guest. The shrill cry brought me to a halt. While I stood there doubtful as to what I should do, Crichton himself emerged from the darkness of the veranda, ran lightly down the steps and disappeared in the shrubbery beside them. A moment later he again came into view with something under his arm. He then came along the beach directly toward me. I was standing in the shadow of a tree. He passed so closely that I could almost have touched him with my outstretched hand, and he stopped not half-a-dozen paces distant. He was not then wearing the sun glasses and his eyes had a vacant, expressionless look. I saw that he was holding the offending rooster. He stood for a moment gently stroking the bird, speaking to it in a gently reproachful manner as one might address a pet dog or an innocently naughty child.

"You shouldn't have made such a racket," he said, "and

[37]

just below the veranda, too. It isn't the first time. Now you're going to receive the punishment you deserve."

With that he took the fowl firmly by the legs, one in each hand, and slowly, deliberately tore it apart. I could hear the smothered rending of the flesh. To say that it was a horrible sight is to say nothing at all, but more horrible still was the expression on Crichton's face. The cock gave one loud squawk but Crichton soon silenced it. He bashed it again and again against the stem of a coconut palm until it was only a shapeless mass of bloody feathers; then he tossed it into the lagoon.

He was dressed in a waistcloth, and his bare chest as well as his hands and face was spattered with blood. Having washed with sea water he dried himself with his *pareu* and sat down on the beach in such a position that he was turned halfway toward me with the moon shining full in his face. I will not venture to say how long he sat thus, quite motionless, his eyes closed as though deep in reverie. At last the shadow of a frown darkened his features and he said, in a low intense voice: "Why did you come here? Did you think I was lonely?"

For two or three seconds I was convinced that he had spoken to me direct, conscious of my presence, and it was only the shock of dismay and astonishment that prevented me from giving myself away. But his air of complete self-absorption reassured me. It was plain that he believed himself alone.

"You are too kind, my friend," he went on. "Too considerate by far. You will forgive me if I deprive myself . . ."

He broke off and was again long silent, sitting with his arms crossed on his knees and his forehead resting against them. I was compelled to stand absolutely motionless, scarcely daring to breathe. He could have heard the slightest sound I might have made. When at last he raised his head, the expression on his face was one of utter hopelessness and desolation, and he said, in a low, broken, heartsick voice: "I don't know what's to come. . . . I don't know. . . ." A moment later he rose and walked slowly back to the house.

I did not see him again. Neither he nor Mama Ruau appeared at the beach the following morning. I went out to the schooner with the first boatload of copra, and being dead tired after my all-night vigil, turned into my bunk and slept heavily. When I came on deck the *Toafa* was headed westward, and Tanao was only a faint bluish haze far to windward. Chan, the least inquisitive of men, asked no questions as to my stay ashore; in fact, as soon as we had left the island it seemed to have dropped completely out of his thoughts.

But I was to hear of Crichton once more at another island where we called for copra. We spent a night there anchored in the lagoon close to the principal village and some natives came aboard to yarn with the sailors. I was lying on deck looking at the stars, paying little attention to their conversation until I heard Tanao mentioned.

One voice said, "Pupuré, the old woman calls him." (That was Crichton's native name, meaning Fair Hair.)

"*Ah, É*" (Oh, yes), a second voice replied. "*Tera popaa. Tera taata haa-moe-hia.*" (That white man. That forgotten one.)

I heard nothing more of Crichton until the evening when Maitua walked into the circle of lamplight on my veranda at Tahiti, bringing me his letter.

* * *

This third voyage seemed interminable; we were at the end of our second week when we sighted Tanao. Under a light breeze we approached slowly and toward midday were within a quarter of a mile of the landing place. The cutter was brought to and Maitua and Nau rowed me ashore. I examined the shore line but saw no sign of life excepting a flock of white terns floating aimlessly over the bush at the far end of the island. We might have been the first men ever to view that lonely place.

Fortunately the sea was calm and we crossed the reef without mishap. Then something I had thought was a round black rock detached itself from the sand and moved down to the edge of the water. It was an umbrella almost completely hiding Ling Foo, who carried it. Maitua and Nau jumped into waist-deep water and guided the boat across the shallows. The umbrella moved away as we approached, up the beach and along the roadway leading to the house. The old Chinese kept well ahead of us, tilting his sunshade now and then to see that we were following. I called to him, but his only reply was to glance back and make a quick beckoning gesture.

Crichton was lying propped up with pillows on a sofa on the veranda. He was shockingly altered, so pale and emaciated that I should not have recognized him, elsewhere. Indeed, I thought for a moment that we had arrived just too late, for his eyes were closed in their deep hollows, his hands folded on his breast, and his face wore the expression of peace and indifference that one sees on the faces of the dead. Ling Foo ran noiselessly across the veranda and stood beside him, looking from Crichton to me and back again. Maitua halted at the top step as though he had been stopped by a viewless barrier. No one spoke. The clock with the ship's-bell attachment was still measuring eternity by seconds. It struck half-past twelve.

Crichton opened his eyes at the sound and stared vacantly before him. "Ling Foo, are you there?" he asked.

The old servant touched him lightly on the shoulder.

"Go down again to the beach. They must be close inshore by this time."

I stepped forward. "We're here, Crichton," I said.

His worn face lighted up. "Please forgive me," he said. "I must have been asleep." He held out his hand, gropingly. "I am deeply grateful."

I could think of nothing to say. The fact that Crichton had no one but me to turn to in his need gave me a truer conception of his aloneness in the world. Nearly a decade had passed since the *Caleb Winship* had brought him here. The events of that well-remembered day, viewed in the light of all that had since happened to me, seemed to have taken place in the course of a previous existence. To find him still here was a shock to my sense of probability, like that one would feel at discovering a man swimming alone in mid-ocean. For all my sympathy I was conscious of a feeling of dull anger against him. What reason or excuse could a man of his age, with the best of life still before him, have had for throwing that life away? What a senseless waste of abilities, of opportunities! And now there would be no more opportunities. He was dying; there was little question of that. It seemed to me that he must have been keeping himself alive for weeks by sheer strength of will.

"I had only a faint hope that you would be able to come," he added; "but I clung to that hope."

"Does the *Toafa* still call here?" I asked.

"Yes, once a year, but she's not due again until September."

He closed his eyes for a moment and lay with his hands outstretched, palms upward. I glanced around the veranda. It was just as I had remembered it; only the man himself had changed. Again he looked dully at the ceiling. "What was it I wanted to say? Oh . . . you must be tired after your voyage. Ling Foo has lunch ready. Afterward, perhaps you would like a siesta? It's very hot here in the middle of the day."

I was glad of an excuse for leaving him for a time. He was very weak and I could see that it tired him to talk. After lunch I returned to the beach with Maitua. Nau had been spearing fish during our absence and had prepared his own food Low Island fashion: raw fish dipped in sea water and eaten with the meat of ripe coconuts. Maitua, through shyness, had eaten sparingly of Ling Foo's luncheon. He joined Nau in his meal and the two men ate with keen appetite, squatting on a coral mushroom beside a pool of water that reflected their faces and the sky. Beyond them was the reef where the surf spouted up in fountains of spume, luminous in the sunlight, and beyond that, the sea, ruffled to the deepest blue by the breeze, and empty save for the cutter a mile offshore. It was a lonely picture, full of harmony and beauty with those natives in the foreground. Maitua and Nau belonged in the setting; they were as much a part of it as the sea fowl skimming along the slopes of the combers. But I had only to imagine Crichton in their place and immediately the beauty seemed to become hostile beauty, and mid-ocean silence the measure of Nature's disapproval of the incongruous element.

When the men had finished their meal I discussed plans with them. They had been long from home and were, I knew, anxious to have news of their families. It seemed useless to keep them waiting at Tanao, the more so as there was no safe anchorage for the cutter. I arranged with them that they should go to their own island of Hao and return within two weeks' time, if possible. The wind was favorable for their voyage and when they had speared some more fish and gathered a supply of green drinking coconuts they rowed out to the cutter, hoisted in their small boat and stood off to the northwest. The little vessel crept up the long slope of the sea until she was lost to view.

It was midafternoon when I returned to the house. Crichton was sleeping; at least I thought he was. A low table stood beside his couch with a glass and a pitcher of water on it and a bell for summoning Ling Foo. I went through to the kitchen connected with the main house by a covered passageway. Here as elsewhere everything was in perfect order. Pots and pans, burnished and shining, hung from hooks along the wall. The stove was brightly polished and sticks of firewood cut at precisely the same length were corded up in a bin nearby. Ling Foo was not there. I returned to the front veranda and seated myself near Crichton's couch. Looking toward him presently I found that he was awake, regarding me with a vacant, and at the same time a thoughtful expression. I awaited, surprised that he didn't speak. At length I forced myself to say, "Is there anything you want, Crichton?"

He started slightly at the sound of my voice. "Oh, I didn't know you were back," he said. "You must have come in very quietly."

"But . . . haven't you seen me sitting here?"

Even as I asked the question I realized that he had not seen me; that he was blind. He then told me what I had almost forgotten until that moment, of the trouble he had had with his eyes, caused by the glare of the sun from the lagoon and the beaches of white sand. He had not realized that it was anything serious and had neglected to take adequate precautions.

"How long have you been like this?" I asked.

"Nearly three years. I can still see the faint outline of objects close by, directly in front of me, but nothing more."

I admired him for his stoicism. He spoke quietly of his loss as though it were a matter of no great importance. "I know the place so well: every foot of beach and nearly every bush and tree. I've not been hampered as much as you might think; and Ling Foo has been a faithful servant, one in a thousand."

"Is Mama Ruau still living?" I asked.

"No, she died two years ago. I've missed her greatly; she was as good to me as a man's own mother could be. She told me that she would always watch over me after her death. It's curious; at times I've been all but convinced of her presence. One has strange fancies in such a lonely place."

"That is an extraordinary old servant of yours," I said. "Does he never speak?"

"Not often. He is a remarkable old chap, never for a moment idle."

"Is he contented here?"

"Yes — quite. I used to urge him to return with Chan Lee to visit his friends on Tahiti, but he's never cared to go."

"And you, Crichton? Have you never left Tanao in all these years?"

"Never," he replied. For a moment the expression on his face grew somber; then he said: "I feel much better. Your coming has done me good."

"I'm delighted to hear you say that," I replied. "By the way, I've let the cutter go. The men were anxious to have news of their families."

"Naturally. I was going to suggest that you do just that. When will they be coming back?"

"Within ten days or two weeks, depending upon the weather. Do you think you might be strong enough by that time to make the voyage to Tahiti? If not, we can hold the cutter here until you are. Will you come?"

He smiled faintly and shook his head.

"To Tahiti? I have a longer voyage than that to make. Don't imagine that I regret it. On the contrary. . . . But let's not discuss my affairs this afternoon. Do you know what I'd like, if it isn't too much of an imposition? I said just now that I'd not minded losing my sight, but I have minded in one respect. I miss my books. Would you be willing to read to me for an hour or so?"

I thought of the last time I had read aloud on his veranda, with such unhappy results, but he seemed to have forgotten that. He was a great admirer of Thoreau and we began with his favorite chapters in *Walden*. Then he asked for *Comus*, and after that for some of Wordsworth's *Lyrical Poems*. Ling Foo brought our supper to the table by Crichton's couch, and he ate with some appetite, for the first time in weeks, he said. Throughout the meal he talked with animation; he seemed to be as starved for conversation as he was for reading. This was a Crichton I had never seen before: urbane, wholly at ease, almost lighthearted in manner. I could not reconcile this view of him with the one I'd had at the time of my second visit.

Afterward when the lamps were lighted I continued reading

whatever he asked for, and it was not until the clock struck ten that he said, "Good Lord! Can it be as late as that?"

I told him that I would gladly continue as long as he liked.

"No, not another word! Thanks ever so much. I can't tell you what a treat this has been for me."

We chatted for a few moments; then I called Ling Foo, who was dozing in a chair by the kitchen table. He brought his sleeping mat and a pillow and spread them on the floor by Crichton's couch in case he should be wanted during the night. I retired to my room — the same room that had been prepared for me at the time of my last visit; but on this occasion I went to bed and slept soundly until morning.

We spent the following morning in settling his affairs. A copy of his will had been filed long since with his attorney in London. He asked me to read over to him his own copy. I was not surprised to learn that he was a man of considerable means. All of his property in England was to be divided equally between a nephew and a niece, his only surviving relatives. What he particularly wished me to do was to send to his attorney — with a personal letter which I wrote at his dictation — the official papers to be secured from the French authorities at Tahiti, establishing the fact of his death. He had something over five hundred pounds on deposit in a Papeete bank, and this money was to go to Ling Foo who had served him so faithfully all these years.

It seemed strange to be discussing these matters with Crichton. He was businesslike, methodical, painstaking. Death was in the background, and yet, because of his quiet, matter-of-fact way of speaking of it, I had no emotional conviction of its nearness. The last thing he asked me to do was to go through his desk and clear out all of his papers and notebooks, including half-a-dozen thick manuscript volumes. These latter, I imagine, contained a personal record of his life at Tanao until the loss of his sight had made writing no longer possible. "Will you please burn all this?" he said. "I shall feel much better when you tell me that it has been destroyed." It required half an hour of poking and stirring the fire to consume the journals, but in the end they were all reduced to ashes.

On the evening of that day Ling Foo and I carried Crichton on his sofa to the open veranda built over the water on the opposite side of the house. It was a glorious night, perfectly still, and not a cloud in the sky. The air was cool and Crichton was covered with a rug. As darkness came on we seemed to be suspended between an upper and nether firmament, so bright and clear were the reflections of the stars in the lagoon. Crichton was weaker than he had been the previous day. The business of settling his affairs had exhausted his little reserve of strength, and he was running a temperature that made him restless and lightheaded. Neither of us spoke for a long time; then he asked for a glass of water which he drank greedily. Presently he roused himself with an effort.

"There is something I have long had on my conscience," he said. "You will remember, when you were last here, my . . . my strange behavior. What must you have thought of me, leaving you like that? . . . And a guest in my own house, too!"

"Don't speak of it, Crichton," I replied. "If apologies are in order let mine come first. I barged in on you without . . ."

He interrupted me.

"No, please! You have nothing to reproach yourself for.

I was guilty of an unpardonable breach of hospitality. I owe you the fullest explanation of my actions on that occasion; but I don't see how I *can* explain without saying more than . . . than you may care to hear. . . . Would you mind if I were to tell you something that I have never spoken of to anyone?"

"No, not if you want to tell me."

"I do want to; but whether it will be possible . . . Let me ask a question: have you ever wondered why I came here to live?"

"Many times."

"What was your supposition?"

"I have never found a satisfactory one. You have always been a puzzle to me, Crichton."

"You're being quite frank? You don't know why I have hidden myself away here?"

"I haven't the slightest idea."

"I believe you. Well, let me get this out, if I can. For some reason I feel a great need to speak, for the first and the last time.

"I am one of those men . . ." He broke off, and after a moment of silence began again. "I am one of those men who . . . who are . . . mistakes of Nature.

"Does this mean anything to you? Do you understand what I am trying to say? Mistakes of Nature . . . tragic, irremediable mistakes. Or experiments, perhaps — who knows? How many there are, of how many kinds! There is one . . . A victim of that blunder in creation is the most unhappy, surely, of all the children of men.

"This sounds maudlin. I am aware of the fact. But I ask you to believe that I am not indulging in self-pity. I gave up that habit long ago. If you like, in this darkness think of me only as a voice, speaking of a man who no longer exists. That is not far from the truth.

"I was in my late teens before I knew. My people never knew. They are all dead now. Three brothers, two older and one younger than myself, were killed during the war. I was the one to be spared. The irony of that fact has given me some bitter moments.

"My boyhood was all that boyhood at its best can be. My parents made comrades of their children and they had no reason to suspect that anything was amiss with one of them. Their desire was to make our childhood happy, and, as we grew older, to help us shape our lives according to our own wishes and abilities. My father believed that education was, in the beginning, a matter of arousing in our minds a disciplined curiosity about life; and in my case he wanted me to be furnished with certain tools to work with: principally languages, both ancient and modern, and mathematics. Thanks to his guidance and encouragement I felt the keenest desire to acquire mastery in the use of these tools, realizing that the drudgery entailed was necessary, and that the tools were not ends in themselves but the means to ends far beyond.

"You may wonder why I speak of this. It is to make clear to you why I remained so long in ignorance of . . . of one side of my nature. If this is not the reason I can assign no other. Unlike my brothers I was not sent to public school but was furnished with private tutors at home where I prepared for the university. I was devoted to hard study and had neither the time nor the inclination for self-exploration on the emotional side. I was more studious than most boys of my years and believed that scholarship was of greater importance than sport. Otherwise, I was not eccentric in any way.

"At seventeen I went up to the university where my father, grandfather and great-grandfather had gone before me. Some of the drudgery of education was past; I now began to know a few, at least, of its delights. And what can equal them? What joy is keener, purer than that of a young man when he first becomes conscious of the unfolding of his powers and looks forward to years of quiet, uninterrupted study? I already knew what my lifework was to be. I had a scholarship in physics, and with the confidence and the arrogance of youth I resolved to be one of the greatest physicists in England.

"In my second year at the university I discovered . . . what, it seems, had to be discovered. It was a gradual revelation, but, in the end, complete. My case may have been exceptional, and from what I now know I think it was. The fact remains that I was unaware of the existence of such . . . of such abnormality until it was revealed to me by a friend and classmate to whom I was deeply devoted. In the long vacation of my second year I went to Germany for further study. It was the worst move I could have made, it seems. What happened there . . . Oh, I'm so mortally tired!"

That cry went to my heart. "Crichton, you needn't go on," I said. "Believe me, I . . ."

"Wait! I beg your pardon," he said. He raised himself on his elbow and his voice became as hard and cold as ice.

"Don't misunderstand me. I was not at the point of making any sordid confessions. Allow me to finish. I have little more to say."

He sank back on his pillow and lay still.

"In Germany I found myself on the brink of an abyss — so at least I conceived of it. I looked down. I saw unhappy creatures like myself moving about in those depths. I pitied them from my heart, but it was loathing that saved me. I differed from them only in this: they had accepted their fate; many of them, I discovered, gloried in it. I would not accept mine — at least I would not accept the common implications of that fate. I saw what I had to do. I gave up my plans for a career. I cut myself off from family and friends. You see, I didn't trust myself. I didn't know what wretched folly friendship might lead me into. I set out in search of some place, preferably an island, where there could be no question of friendship, not even of companionship. When I found that place, I remained . . . as you know."

He died very peacefully three days later. I was sitting with him and we had talked a little of common things; then he fell into a quiet sleep. About an hour afterward he awoke and asked me to help him turn on his side. That was the last time he spoke.

Ling Foo and I buried him at the spot he had chosen. It was not in the cemetery at the far end of the islet, but near the lagoon beach at the head of the small cove that could be seen from his house. In accordance with his own wishes, no stone, not even a border of sea shells, was placed to mark his grave. It is marked, adequately and beautifully, by the shadows of palm fronds moving to and fro over the coral sand.

II. Captain Handy's Memoirs

It was during a voyage with Chan Lee, owner of the schooner *Toafa*, to some of the remoter islands of the far-flung Low Archipelago, that I first met Monsieur Clémont. His house, in the European style, stood on the lagoon beach near the center of the village. Although not large as houses go in other parts of the world, it towered like a palace above the native huts surrounding it. The roof was covered with rusty sheets of corrugated iron and the eaves were ornamented with a great deal of gingerbread scrollwork. A faded French flag hung from a staff slanted out over the stairway leading to the veranda. I asked Chan whose house it was.

"Flenchman, half-caste, got native mama," he replied, as we were coming in to the anchorage. "He belong Gover'ment. Get dless up now. Bimeby he come."

When he did come, one of the *Toafa's* reef boats was lowered and Chan and I were rowed ashore. My host — at least, I hoped he was to be that — met us at the end of a rickety landing stage. He was a stout man of middle age, swarthy in complexion, with iron-gray hair and blue-gray eyes. He was dressed very warmly for the tropics in a double-breasted woolen suit, a white shirt with an old-fashioned "choker" collar, a black derby hat and yellow shoes. The shoes, evidently, were much

too small for him. He kept shifting his weight from one foot
to the other; the sweat streamed down his face, and the stiff
collar had melted by the time we had reached him. He greeted
me in fluent French, but Chan having told him that I was an
American he immediately changed to English, which he spoke
with a quaintness I cannot hope to render here. There was
something gentle and deprecatory in his manner, and his smile
was so genuinely friendly that my heart warmed to him at
once. He presented me with a card which read:

> Monsieur Raoul Clémont
> *Administrateur*
> *Hopéaroa*

I asked if I might stay at the island until the return of the
Toafa two or three weeks later.

"You wish to do so?" he replied, his broad face beaming.
"Then it shall arrange. You shall stay at my house. This is the
greatest honor for me."

Immediately he gave orders to one of Chan Lee's sailors to
fetch my things. Having introduced me Chan returned aboard,
for there was some merchandise to be sent ashore and he
wanted to get away as early as possible. I followed my host
to his house.

The loud squeaking of his shoes seemed to give voice to the
pain they caused him. I was relieved when he asked if he
might remove them.

"Please do," I said. "Make yourself comfortable."

He informed me that he wore his *popaa* clothing only upon
the rare occasions when a schooner arrived. He returned a
moment later, barefoot, but he had put on another stiff collar which melted at once, as the first had done. I was tempted

to suggest that he remove his heavy serge coat and trousers, but he seemed to feel that his position as administrator demanded the European style clothing, for the moment at least.

My arrival appeared to be an important event and he was evidently pleased at having some official business to transact. He conducted me to his "bureau" where he spent a good hour getting me registered as a temporary resident at Hopéaroa. He transcribed my passport word for word in his ledger, beginning with the "Notice" on the inside front cover, and ending with the six abstracts from the passport regulations at the back.

"I wish to have everything in due process of law," he explained, so I waited while he wrote everything out in a neat Spencerian hand. While copying the "Caution" on the inside cover which tells what is to be done if a passport is lost, he halted to read aloud this sentence: "New passports in such cases can be issued only after exhaustive inquiry."

"Exhaustive . . . exhaustive," he repeated, musingly. "I have forgotten this meaning. But no! I remember! When I am tired I say I am exhaustive. This is true?"

I explained the sense of it and he thanked me with warmth and sincerity, as though I had done him an important service. Upon reaching the "Description of Bearer" he again paused and looked at me with an expression of deep respect.

"My guest! You are an *écrivain!* You write and write, and many people read what you write! This is the greatest honor for me. What journal in America have you the duty to be their author?"

"Oh, I'm not really an author," I replied. "As a matter of fact . . ."

He thought I was being modest.

"But you shall be!" he insisted, eagerly. "Your government says you are author — *écrivain*. The Se*crétaire de l'État* of your great nation" — he turned for reference to the passport — "wishes your value to be known. You are *écrivain,* he writes. You must be safe and free, and have all lawful aid and protection."

I wish I could convey an impression of the seriousness with which he said this. Had I been carrying a personal letter from the President of the United States it could hardly have made a more profound impression than my passport had done.

"Here, too, you shall write," he said. "You shall meet Captain Handy. His life is of great deeds and he wishes his memoirs to be written into a book. How glad he shall be if you will help him with his history!"

I had seen Captain Handy's schooner as we entered the Hopéaroa lagoon, and Chan Lee had spoken briefly of the captain himself.

"Dlink, dlink, alltime dlink," he said. "Plitty soon he finish."

His ship, considerably larger than the *Toafa,* lay at anchor about one hundred yards offshore. The paint of her topsides, once white, was now a dirty yellow blistered and peeling. The seams gaped, and streams of rust extended from her chain plates to the luxuriant growth of marine vegetation that covered her bottom. The standing rigging hung slack, and the ends of the springstay, which had parted, dangled from the masts, swaying gently with the imperceptible motion of the vessel. An awning made of pieces of canvas and bits of copra sacking stitched together was stretched over the main boom. The only sign of life aboard the ship was an old native who looked as ancient as the vessel, working the handle of a ship's pump. He moved slowly back and forth with the regularity of the pendulum on a grandfather's clock, and a small stream of clear water, its flow keeping time with his movements, gushed over the ship's side. Chan told me the vessel had been lying there for years.

Having spoken of Captain Handy, Monsieur Clémont suggested that we should go out to visit him. I had a good deal of curiosity to see the captain of this ancient vessel that looked as though it were kept afloat by the old man at the pump. I made some inquiries while we were paddling out to her, but my host told me only what I already knew, that the ship had been long at Hopéaroa. He gave me to understand that I would learn everything from the captain himself.

The canoe was made fast alongside and we clambered aboard. The man at the pump looked at us with a worried expression and said something in a low voice to Monsieur Clémont, who hesitated for a moment and then turned to me.

"All day the captain sleeps," he said. "Perhaps he shall be unwilling that I speak to him now, but your coming is the great reason. He should know this."

I followed him down the companionway into a cabin as dirty and dilapidated as the rest of the vessel. A table in the middle of the floor was heaped with old newspapers and dog-eared story magazines. A tin lamp with a rusty shade hung above the table. Against one wall was a curtained recess. Monsieur Clémont stood irresolutely before it; then, with the air of making a heroic decision, he put back the curtain, revealing a bunk over a chest of drawers. There lay Captain Handy, asleep.

He was naked to the waist, and his body was incredibly thin and hairy. His temples were deep hollows and his skull quite bald on top, but the hair of his beard reached almost to his waist. His head was long and lean and angular; his lower jaw had fallen open and he was breathing noisily through his mouth. His skin was the color of fungus, as though it had not been touched by sunlight in many months. I was conscious of a feeling of uneasiness and repulsion as I looked at this inert figure. He seemed scarcely human.

Monsieur Clémont touched him lightly on the shoulder and then drew back, glancing at me with a frightened expression, as though he had committed an unheard-of indiscretion. There was no response.

"He's a sound sleeper," I remarked. "You'd better shake him, hadn't you?"

After a good deal of hesitation he did so, very gently. The mouth snapped shut, and the captain made a frightful grimace as though he had bitten into something nauseating.

"All right, all right," he muttered, petulantly. His voice was surprisingly deep and resonant. It was hard to realize that so great a volume of sound could come so easily from such a ghost of a man. Then he opened his eyes, glassy-blue and cold. The light of recognition came into them slowly, but once it had he raised himself to a sitting position.

"What's this?" he roared.

"Captain, you will excuse me? The *Toafa* is here. We have a visitor . . ."

The old man got to his knees and grasped the edge of his bunk, and at the same moment Monsieur Clémont seemed to be pushed by invisible hands backward to the companion-way where he stood regarding me in a frightened, apologetic manner. The captain remained motionless for a moment staring at vacancy. The baleful light died from his eyes; the muscles of his face relaxed and his head drooped forward as though

its weight were too much for his strength. He balanced unsteadily on his knees; then collapsed on his side and lay still.

Monsieur Clémont glanced at me sorrowfully as we returned to the deck.

"I was too bold," he said. "In the daytime Captain Handy
sleeps, and he is uneasy to be wakened."

"Is he always like that?" I asked.

"Oh, no! You shall not think of him by this meeting. In the
evening time when he has had his breakfast, you shall see.
I shall tell him you are *écrivain, journaliste*. He shall be glad.
And he plays the zither. I am never tired to listen."

Chan Lee was awaiting us at Monsieur Clémont's store (he
was both administrator and storekeeper at Hopéaroa). The
breeze had freshened and, as the current was now flowing out
of the lagoon, he wished to sail at once. He informed me that
he would call again at the island on the return voyage within
two or three weeks, depending upon the weather. We watched
the *Toafa* until she was beyond the passage; then Monsieur
Clémont showed me my room. I saw at once that it was his
own but he insisted that I should occupy it.

"I have not often a guest from the great world," he said.
"Not since eight years has a visitor come. This shall be a happy
souvenir for me."

He told me that he was born at Hopéaroa and had never
lived elsewhere. "My mother is of this island," he said. "You
have understood, perhaps, that I am of the French blood by
my father? He was an honored man of that great nation. See,
he is there!"

On the wall above a table was a framed photograph of a
French naval officer in full-dress uniform. Despite his black
beard I could see the likeness between this man and Monsieur

Clémont. One hand rested on a pedestal and the other was clasped lightly around the hilt of his sword. Across the bottom of the photograph was written:

A ma petite Manukura
Souvenir affectueux de nos promenades sur la belle isle
de Hopéaroa.

Raoul Clémont

Capne de Frégate
Le 5 Août, 1875

"I wish to have known my father," he said, wistfully. "His ship of war came but once to Hopéaroa. Manukura is my mother. She loved him but she heard of him no more. She gave me his name. But you shall see a beautiful picture of my father I have had made from this one. It is in my mother's room."

He led me down a narrow hallway to the other end of the house.

"My mother has lost her health since five years," he said. "Now she remains in her bed."

He rapped gently, then opened the door and motioned me to follow. We entered a large chamber filled with furniture upholstered in faded red plush. A brass lamp ornamented with glass pendants hung from the center of the ceiling, and the walls were covered with a variety of shell ornaments in beautiful designs and colors. But my attention was first attracted to the bed where my host's mother lay, propped up with pillows. Her face was full of beauty and character, and I could imagine how lovely she must have been as a young girl. Although she was now a woman of seventy her hair was but lightly streaked with gray. It was parted in the middle and lay in two thick braids on the counterpane. Her son addressed her in the native tongue, explaining who I was. While he did so she took one of my hands and held it. I could not doubt the sincerity of her welcome.

She spoke to her son at some length. When she had finished, he said:

"My mother wishes to know if you have heard in other lands of my father, *le Capitaine de Frégate,* Raoul Clémont?"

I confessed, reluctantly, that I had not, adding that doubtless I would have heard of him had I been of French nationality.

The colored enlargement hung on the wall facing her bed. With its huge gilt frame it must have covered twelve square feet. The cheeks and lips were red, the hair and beard a bluish black; the uniform a bright blue, and the sword, buttons and epaulettes, gilt. Every line and wrinkle had been smoothed out of the face, which resembled that of a wax figure. On the mat, in one corner, was printed: "Midwest Art-Photo Company, Chicago, Illinois, U.S.A."

Having returned to my room I examined some English books on a shelf above the table. I was surprised to find on that remote island an edition of Tennyson's *Poems,* Jeremy Taylor's *Rule and Exercises of Holy Dying,* Charles Lamb's *Essays,* and a volume of *Selected English and American Poems.* The four volumes had been well thumbed and a French-English conversation manual had been worn to tatters with use. Monsieur Clémont told me they had belonged to a Protestant missionary who had lived on the island and who died there many years ago.

"He was so good to me," he said. "He gave me the lessons in English. Since then I am aptly self-taught. Often I read in these books. I know how to say many poesies in your language. Should you wish to hear one?"

He then recited with fervor and with quaint mispronunciations some lines from Tennyson's "Maud":

> Come into the garden, Maud,
> For the black bat, Night, has flown . . .

I commended him warmly at the close and he was much pleased.

"Yes," he said, "I speak the English well, but the writing I cannot. How I should wish to do this! Then I should have pleasure to compose. I should help Captain Handy with his memoirs. . . . If you would help him," he added, eagerly, "he would be happy. He says they must be printed in a book. He will be a rich man when this is done."

"Chan Lee tells me that he drinks rather heavily," I remarked.

"It is true; he has too much of the drink," he replied, sadly.

In questioning him further about the captain I learned that his schooner had been lying four years in the Hopéaroa lagoon and that the captain still had rum aboard. The vessel was so ancient as to be no longer seaworthy, but the captain had hope of refitting her. He was convinced that, if he could complete his memoirs and secure a publisher for them, they would find a wide and eager public and the returns from the sale of them would provide him with ample funds for the repair of his ship.

I questioned Monsieur Clémont as to how Captain Handy managed to live, meanwhile. He avoided a direct answer by telling me of the captain's zither playing, which was so beautiful, he said, that it often brought tears to his eyes. I concluded that Monsieur Clémont himself had been furnishing Captain Handy with food from his store, on credit. I was convinced of this later when, returning from a walk to the far end of the islet, I saw several canoes going out to the schooner. As they came alongside I heard the captain's booming voice: "What's this? My supplies?" I guessed that Monsieur Clémont, who was the soul of courtesy, had wished to spare the captain's feelings by sending him at night, as unobtrusively as possible, some of the supplies he had received by the *Toafa*. If he had been doing this for four years, it seemed to me that he was paying rather heavily for the captain's zither playing, however ravishing that might be.

Upon returning to the settlement I found the natives standing in line before my host's store which adjoined his house, and he was passing out to them the newly arrived provisions.

"My guest! I have searched for you," he said. "I have seen Captain Handy. He wishes to greet you."

"Has he come ashore?" I asked.

"No, he comes not often to the land. But I have told him you are *journaliste*. He is pleased. He wishes to offer you to prepare his history."

"Couldn't we wait until tomorrow?" I suggested.

He regarded me with an expression of concern.

"Of course! You are tired and wish for your sleep. Tomorrow evening we will go. Now you shall rest in your bed."

But I was not sleepy so I remained at the store while Monsieur Clémont and his assistant continued to distribute supplies: rice, tinned beef, pickles, and the like. The mere sight of those tins of bully beef made me feel squeamish at the stomach. It brought back the very feel of the war and the feel of night in the desolate area of the front-line positions in

[62]

Flanders, with the ration parties coming up the communication trenches with the next day's provisions. In the imagination I could see the intense eerie light of Very rockets revealing the wastes of no-man's-land and hear the chatter of machine-gun fire and the wail of ricochets dying away in the distance. I was momentarily aware of the smell of lyddite, gas, decaying human flesh, and the peculiar odor of trenches and damp dugouts filled with unwashed men. No ex-soldier, surely, can ever again look with complacency at a tin of beef.

There were, apparently, no ex-soldiers among the people of Hopéaroa. It was not only tinned beef that they craved, but sour pickles as well. Large quantities were disposed of. No money changed hands nor was there any bookkeeping. Monsieur Clémont informed me that there was no need to keep a record of his sales. Everyone knew what he had bought, and would pay for his purchases in copra before the return of Chan Lee's schooner.

"I keep store only these few days when the *Toafa* comes," he explained. "Then no more food. All is finished."

Certainly, a large amount of it was being finished on this first evening. I never again expect to see such a beef-and-pickle orgy. Some who had overestimated their capacity for sour pickles were groaning with faint dolefulness, but their misery had not the slightest deterrent effect upon those whose pickles were yet to be consumed. The same thing happened every time the *Toafa* came, Monsieur Clémont informed me. "They like so much these foods, and they are not usted to them. Always afterwards there are stomach pains."

He bade me good night at the door of my room. "I hope you shall sleep with comfort," he said, and as I had eaten but a fragment of one pickle which was too sour for my taste, I did sleep soundly until morning.

As a matter of fact I didn't wake until nine o'clock. My host had slipped a note under my door. "Good morning," it read. "Your coffee shall be ready for you when you wish it. You shall find me at my store," and there I joined him a little later. He had just opened another packing case, and had laid out on his counter a dozen large funeral wreaths of imitation flowers made of colored glass beads strung on wire framework — the kind one saw in every French cemetery back of the trenches. Evidently the holocaust of 1914–1918 had not fulfilled the expectations of the makers of such wreaths, and the surplus stocks were being disposed of wherever a market for them could be found. They bore ornate beaded inscriptions twined among the flowers: "Mort pour la France," "Mort pour la Patrie," and the like. Monsieur Clémont stood before them, lost in admiration.

"These shall be so beautiful in our cemetery," he said. He carried one to the doorway to examine it under a better light, and turned to me immediately with an exclamation of astonishment.

"My guest! Captain Handy is coming! Never he comes to the land since long time. He wishes to greet you!"

He brought out two chairs and placed a small table between them; then hurried to his house and returned with two glasses and a pitcher of water. Meanwhile, the captain, who was being rowed ashore by one of his retainers, had almost reached the wharf.

"Way enough!" he roared, and then, "Stern all!" as though in command of at least a dozen oarsmen. The old native backed on his oars and made fast at the end of the pier. The captain climbed the ladder, and with the sailor following at a respectful distance, came slowly up the beach. Under a wide-brimmed pith helmet, with his white beard streaming out from beneath, he looked like a disreputable cousin of Father Time. Monsieur Clémont went out to meet him, but he waved him aside without speaking and entered the store. He gave me a nod, sat down, and with his hands braced on his knees breathed heavily, as though the short walk from the pier had nearly exhausted him.

"Warm," he observed, and again I gave an inward start at the deep sonorous voice issuing from the corpselike body.

I agreed that it was.

He turned his head slightly, and the old retainer who was standing behind his chair stepped forward and placed a bottle on the table.

"Have a drink?" he asked, and taking my willingness for granted he poured out two half-tumblers of rum. He took a generous swallow from his own.

"Well, sir," he said, smacking his lips and sucking in on his handlebar mustache, "I understand you're going to pay us a visit. This your first trip in the Pacific?"

I told him that I'd come from San Francisco six months ago.

"Hmm! I've been out here fifty-two years."

"As long as that! You must know these islands pretty well."

"I'd like to meet the man, white or Kanaka, that knows 'em better. But they're not what they were. You ought to have been here in the seventies. Then you'd have had something to write about. Our friend, here," with a contemptuous nod toward Monsieur Clémont, "tells me you're an author."

"Hardly that," I replied. "I'm merely traveling. I've always wanted to visit the South Seas."

He poured himself another drink.

"That's right. Keep your business to yourself. That's been my practice. I reckon story writers are like the rest of us: they want a free field if they can get it and no competition. Ever hear of a man named Becke?"

"Becke? Do you mean Louis Becke?" I asked.

"That's the one. He traded out here years ago, and did a lot of writing on the side."

"Oh, yes. I've read many of his stories."

"They say he made a pile of money out of 'em?"

"That may be," I replied. "Some of his books are still in print. Did you know him by any chance?"

"Know him? I got the best of Louis Becke on many a deal in the old days. But I wouldn't have thought he had it in him to be an author."

"His tales have the stamp of truth on them," I remarked; "and they're written simply. Readers like that."

The captain snorted contemptuously.

"Truth? I can tell you more truth about the South Seas in twenty minutes than Louis Becke could have told you in twenty years. And that's what I've come to see you about," he added. "I've got an offer to make you."

Again he turned his head, and the old native who watched his every move placed before him a parcel wrapped in brown paper.

"As I said," he went on, "I been fifty-two years in the Pacific. I know it from the Carolines to Easter Island as well as you know the back of your hand. Romance? Adventure? I've had more of it in a day than most men have in a lifetime. Well, the last two or three years I been writin' out some of my recollections. I got 'em in the back of this old ledger; not everything, of course, but some of the most interestin' ones. Now what I want you to do is this: take this book, read it over, print it out for me on your writin' machine on nice paper, put in all the fancywork you want to about wavin' palms and blue lagoons, and when you go back to America get it made into a proper book for me. Here's a chance you won't have again in your whole life. It'll sell like hot cakes, you needn't worry about that, and I'll go halves with you. We'll split, fifty-fifty. How's that? Fair enough?"

"Don't you think it would be better if it was all your own work?" I asked. "I might spoil it, tampering with it."

"Sure it would," he replied. "You'll find you won't have much to do except dressin' it up a bit and layin' it out in chapters. I don't know anything about that kind of monkey business."

I tried to excuse myself, but it was useless. He thought I was merely holding out for better terms. By that time he had more than half emptied the rum bottle, and the more he drank the more convinced he became that he had written a masterpiece. He went on at great length to assure me that I would have little to do except to make a fair copy of his manuscript and carry it to some publisher.

"It's all there," he said, laying his hand on the parcel; "and better as it stands than any story Louis Becke ever wrote. Wait till you read it! Man, there's a fortune in it! But mind! I want my share. I'll go fifty-fifty and not a penny above it!"

"It's not that," I again explained, and so it went on. I was surprised to see that cadaverous old man — he looked as though he might drop dead at any minute — carry his liquor so well. Its only apparent effect upon him was to make him more loquacious and argumentative, to accentuate the bell-like quality of his voice, and to deepen his conviction, both that he had a masterpiece here and that I was angling for the lion's share in the proceeds from the sale of it. At last I agreed to read it. He pushed the parcel across the table, and, keeping his hand on it, drew down his eyebrows and regarded me suspiciously.

"I can trust you?" he asked.

"You'll have to if you leave it with me," I replied.

He weighed the matter and decided that the risk must be taken. Then he tried to pour himself another drink. Noticing that the bottle was empty, he rose.

"Time to go aboard," he said.

He grasped the corner of the table, swaying slightly. The old retainer gave him his pith helmet and made a timid offer of assistance, but the captain threw off his arm and walked gingerly to the door. I watched with concern as he went along the rickety wharf and down the ladder to his skiff. He managed it without accident, however, took the tiller and ordered his man to push off. When a little distance out he turned with difficulty in his seat and looked back, holding his helmet against the sun.

"Be careful of that ledger," he called. "And mind! Fifty-fifty! Not a penny more!"

It was then past midday and oppressively hot and still. Everyone at Hopéaroa slept during the heat of the day; in fact, repose was the principal island occupation. The islanders could lie down anywhere, at any time, and go to sleep at once, as dogs and cats do. After lunch, observing that my host was getting drowsy, I excused myself, put on my pyjamas and lay down on the bed in an attempt to cool off. It was a good time, I thought, to examine Captain Handy's memoirs, so I propped the ledger against my knees and opened it.

It had a bouquet like that of an empty rum keg, and there was no doubt that a good deal of liquor had been spilled on its pages. The front of the book was filled with notations of business transactions, the sale of various kinds of trade goods to the islanders, the earliest of which had taken place between thirty and forty years ago. I observed that Captain Handy's profit was never less than 200 per cent and often more. The memoirs filled about one hundred and fifty pages in the back of the volume, written in pencil, in a quavery hand. I began with page one:

FIFTY YEARS IN THE PACIFIC
Or
THE LIFE OF GEORGE C. HANDY

There's been a lot of books about the South Sea Islands and most of them are not worth the paper they're printed on. I ought to know. I've traded in the Pacific for fifty years as my title shows, and if anybody knows the ways of kanakas I do. I've decided to write down some of my recollections, and reader when you've finished this book if you don't wish there was more of it I'll miss my guess.

I'll begin at the time when I was supercargo on the *Turia* that belonged to Wyatt & McClintock of Papeete. That was in 1872 when the kanakas would take anything you'd a mind to sell and pay anything you'd a mind to ask. They didn't pay money of course, they didn't have any, but they'd give you pearls and pearl shells and copra which is as good as money any day.

Old Joe Cheeseman was captain of the *Turia*. He didn't care any more about fifty centimes than he did about his right eye and that was okay with me. All we had for cargo was some cheap laundry soap, some kegs of salt beef, some calico and overalls, and about ten cases full of bottles of iodine and physic pills. Well, this trip we went first to Tikehau. There's a good pass into the lagoon at this island and we anchored in front of the village. The kanakas paddled out and we said we'd give them a box of laundry soap, six pairs of overalls and twenty yards of calico for every ton of copra they brought us. We laid up there till we had fifteen tons, then we went to Rairoia. They had a lot of pearls. We got a tobacco-sack full, A–1 quality, and all we paid for them was a case of physic pills. We said the medicine was good for anything from sore throat to rheumatism. We had good luck all that voyage and went back to Papeete with seventy tons of copra and pearl shell and a cigar box full of fine pearls.

The next trip we went to the south'ard. We carried about the same cargo only instead of laundry soap we had eight barrels of rum and a lot of cheap mouth organs. Kanakas are a lazy lot as everyone knows who has to deal with them, but when you got something they want they'll work for it. That's because they got nothing of their own except coconuts and fish. In these days of course trading is nothing to what it was in the seventies and eighties. We loaded the schooner again in no time and most of the cargo was paid for with the eight barrels of rum and twenty dollars' worth of mouth organs.

I read on for a dozen pages, then dipped into the record farther along, and it was all like this. It seemed incredible that a man who had spent half a century in the Pacific voyaging among widely scattered islands and archipelagoes should have found nothing worthy of record but his trading ventures. There was something awe-inspiring in his singleness of purpose and interest, which was to get as much as he could from the islanders and to give as little as possible in return. Occasionally, I found passages such as the following: "We landed at Puka Puka and found a big powwow going on — singing and dancing and all that. . . . Three men came riding in over the reef with a big sea turtle they'd taken with their hands, so they didn't want none of our salt beef." Such passages were as near as he would come to any description of native life and customs. I searched for an hour, and the only passage I found to relieve the bleak monotony of the narrative was this:

When we was coming up from Mangareva, Joe (Cheeseman) got sick. We didn't have any medicine aboard except the physic pills we'd been passing off on kanakas. I asked Joe if he wanted some and he said he guessed he could get along without. He got worse and worse and was out of his head part of the time. He kept saying, "Put me ashore, George, put me ashore." He was afraid of dying at sea. So when we came to an island not far off our course we took him over the reef in the whaleboat and came near getting swamped doing it. It was a godforsaken place no people on it. He was thirsty for coconut water so I gave him some. I guess he knew he was going to die and the next day he did. Just before he passed out he said, "Don't you bury me at sea, George. Leave me here." So we did. We got to Papeete two weeks later.

I put the ledger on the table and took down one of Monsieur Clémont's English books — Jeremy Taylor's *Rule and Exercises of Holy Dying* — but because of the sultriness of the afternoon, perhaps, the text soon blurred before my eyes and I fell asleep.

I was awakened by a knock at the door and was surprised to find it quite dark in the room. "Come in," I called, and my host entered.

"My guest! I have disturbed your sleep," he said, apologetically. "But the food is ready."

After a plunge in the lagoon I felt greatly refreshed and did full justice to a supper of delicious baked flying fish and *taro poi*. While we were in the midst of the meal a note was brought in from Captain Handy asking us to come out to his ship that evening. He said he had something important to tell me.

We found him at the cabin table with a bottle of rum before him. He took it for granted that I had spent the afternoon reading his story.

"Well, what do you think of it?" he asked, at once.

He awaited my reply with such eagerness that I hadn't the heart to disappoint the old man. So I said, which was true, that I thought it a remarkable document.

"Didn't I tell you?" he replied, triumphantly. "But I haven't wrote the half of what I might. That's what I want to see you about."

He began a long account of other experiences which he now believed should be included in the memoirs, and I sat there making brief replies, again marveling at his capacity for rum. I asked some questions, hoping to get him started on something interesting, but I might just as well have saved my breath. An hour passed and still he rambled on. Finally, Monsieur Clémont, who had scarcely spoken all evening, said, "Captain, should you wish to play on the zither?" I warmly seconded the proposal and the captain told Monsieur Clémont to fetch it from a drawer under his bunk. We waited while he tuned some of the strings. Then, tucking his beard under the table, he began.

I didn't know what to expect, and, certainly, I was not prepared for the performance which followed. At first he played some simple pieces — waltzes, marches, and the like, to limber up his fingers, but each number was more difficult than the one preceding. When he played "I Dreamt That I Dwelt in Marble Halls," and "Listen to the Mocking-Bird," his fingers were all but invisible as they flew over the strings. But "Larboard Watch" was the most remarkable performance. He sang this to his own accompaniment, and when he came to the refrain,

> Larboard watch, ahoy!
> Larboard watch, ahoy!

his virtuosity with the instrument at the end of each line was truly wonderful. And for depth and volume his singing voice even surpassed his speaking voice. Indeed, it seemed miraculous, coming from a man well into his seventies who was nothing but skin and bones and beard.

Had he continued singing and playing in the manner of "Larboard Watch," I could have listened with pleasure all night; but at last he became muddled, which was not surprising, considering the amount of rum he had drunk. He tried a few other songs but made increasingly sorry work with them. He pushed the instrument aside.

"No use," he said. "Can't sing an' more."

He glared at Monsieur Clémont and me in puzzled fashion and presently he began calling me "Joe." Evidently he thought I was his old trading partner, Captain Cheeseman.

"You gwan that bus'ness, Joe," he said. "Lot o' money in it, both of us. I'll trust you, but mind you don't try any your monkey tricks! Fifty-fifty — fair enough, ain't it? 'Sfars I'll go, anyway."

Presently his glazed eyes rested upon Monsieur Clémont. He pointed a limp skinny finger at him.

"Joe, what that Kanaka doin' here? Owe him anything? Give him bottle physic pills . . . tell him run along."

His utterance became thicker and thicker, and a few minutes later he passed out completely. He would have fallen off his chair had not Monsieur Clémont sprung forward to catch him. He carried him to his bunk and covered him with a dirty bedspread, tucking the edges gently around his shoulders. Then, having put the zither carefully back in its drawer, he extinguished the light. The faint radiance of the last quarter moon streaming through a porthole fell upon the captain's face, silvering his beard and the tufts of snowy hair at his temples. He was in a profound stupor, but he looked like some ancient holy man, sleeping peacefully after a supper of herbs and water.

"Does this happen often, Monsieur Clémont?" I asked as we were paddling ashore.

"Yes, but today is more unusual than before. He has failed his sleep." After a silence, he added, "I should wish to play on the zither like Captain Handy."

I supposed we should see nothing more of the captain for a day or two at least, but the following afternoon he again came ashore. It had been raining during the early part of the afternoon and I was writing some letters to be posted upon my return to Tahiti. The natives had never before seen a typewriter and half the village had assembled in front of the veranda where I was at work. Monsieur Clémont was as deeply interested as any of them. He thought a typewriter a marvelous instrument, which it is, in fact. He asked whether I would mind letting the others come up to see how it worked. I was glad to comply, so he lined them up and brought them forward one by one to look over my shoulder for a minute or two. He made them keep absolute silence, and finding it difficult to compose even letters under those circumstances, I wrote and rewrote: "Now is the time for all good men to come to the aid of the party." I had covered several pages with this immortal sentence by the time Captain Handy appeared.

He thought I was transcribing the memoirs and was greatly disappointed to learn that I had not yet begun the work. Being in an indulgent mood, I decided that I might as well make an afternoon of it, so I copied half-a-dozen pages to show him how it looked in print. This was a great mistake, for he came again the following day, and the day after that, and continued to pay me daily visits, always followed by the old retainer, carrying the usual bottle. He looked more and more haggard, for the loss of his daylight sleep and the increased consumption of rum were telling on him severely. Then, strangely enough, the ledger disappeared.

I knew that it was not lost, and meanwhile I was relieved of the dreary task of copying it. But the captain became increasingly suspicious, and shortly after its disappearance he accused me of stealing it. His opinion of the story, never a modest one as I have indicated, had risen enormously and he really thought I meant to smuggle it away with me and rob him of his 50 per cent. I tried to reassure him but only succeeded in thoroughly convincing him of my guilt. I decided to let matters take their course for a few days to see what would happen. To my surprise he made an official complaint before Monsieur Clémont, *Administrateur.*

His position was a delicate one. Here was I, his guest, and an *écrivain* for whom the Secretary of State of the United States of America had asked a safe and free passage through foreign lands, and "all lawful aid and protection," accused of theft by Captain Handy who had had a life of great deeds and who played so beautifully on the zither. He informed me of the complaint with a delicacy and tact which would have done credit to a French ambassador.

"But Monsieur Clémont!" I said. "You don't really believe that I have stolen his ledger, do you? It must be somewhere in your house."

"My guest! I should never believe this! But Captain Handy exacts you. I am *Administrateur.* It is my duty to accept his complaining. But you shall see. You shall be excused by due process of law."

So he made out the complaint in French. It was a curious document stating the circumstances and the nature of Captain Handy's accusation. I had the honor of copying it for him on my typewriter, the first legal document, I believe, ever "uttered" at Hopéaroa. But before the trial could take place the ledger was found. It had slipped down at the head of my bed and worked in under the mattress.

To prevent any further complications I made an excursion to an islet on the far side of the lagoon. I took some fishhooks and line, a light blanket and nothing in the way of provisions but some salt and a box of matches, for I wanted to see whether I could support myself for a few days in something like the native fashion.

Monsieur Clémont took me across in a sailing canoe. No one

lived on this other islet, but there were two or three small huts used by the natives when they came over to fish or make copra. I asked my host not to return for me until the end of the week.

I had a gloriously lonely time. My only fear was that Monsieur Clémont might come back too soon, or bring Captain Handy over. Fortunately, on the second day it began to blow, and the wind increased steadily, so that it would have been impossible for anyone to cross without great trouble from the village island which was dead to leeward. It was an awe-inspiring sight, particularly at night, to see the surf pile up on the reef. The great swells seemed to rise higher than the land, and fell with a thundering shock which shook the little islet to its foundations. I thought my hut would be blown away, and, in fact, one of the empty ones was demolished. Despite the wind it was clear weather and I spent the days and most of the nights in the open.

On the Saturday it fell calm again, and I saw the canoe returning. As it neared the islet, I gathered from Monsieur Clémont's manner that something unusual had happened. I was not mistaken. Captain Handy was dead. It had happened three days before. The captain's old retainer had found him in the morning, stretched out on the cabin floor near his bunk. He had been dead for some hours.

"It was needed to bury him at once," Monsieur Clémont said. "I should have wished to come for you but this was prevented by the strong wind. We gave him the funeral that afternoon."

He spoke gravely of the captain's death but with no display of trumped-up emotion. Nevertheless I could see that he was genuinely touched at thought of this old man, so friendless, save for the one old seaman, and so homeless save for his decayed ruin of a schooner.

The ship looked even more forlorn than usual, I thought. The soul had quite gone out of her now, but the old retainer was still at the pump. I wondered whether he would ever be able to stop pumping, having done it for so long. We passed close alongside, and through the clear water I could see innumerable rusty tins lying beneath her.

"Monsieur Clémont," I said, "I wish you would tell me something."

He glanced at me inquiringly.

"It's none of my business, of course, but have you been supplying Captain Handy with provisions all these years?"

"Since three years," he said. "He was an aged man and he had no money. There was no one else to help him. This was my duty."

He volunteered no further information and I did not press him for any, but as we were walking out to the cemetery he said, "Should you think I might have Captain Handy's zither?"

I told him I thought he was fully entitled to it.

The cemetery was on the ocean beach, half a mile from the village. A wooden cross had been erected over the captain's grave, and leaning against it was one of Monsieur Clémont's beaded funeral wreaths which bore the inscription, "Tombé sur le Champs d'Honneur." My host removed his hat and I followed his example.

"He was a man of great deeds," he said. "He is sleeping now."

I nodded, without speaking.

"Should you wish to continue with his memoirs?" he asked, after a brief silence.

"Oh, I don't know . . ." I replied. Then it occurred to me that I might do something to perpetuate Captain Handy's memory, to carry out his wishes, after a fashion. I had very little money left after my six months of wandering. And, after all, journalism was my trade. If I could write a little story perhaps I might be able to sell it to some editor . . .

Then I heard, or thought I heard, a deep, muffled, sepulchral voice issuing from the newly made grave:

"Now mind! Fifty-fifty!"

III. Sing: A Song of Sixpence

In those days, while living at the Aina Paré, a hotel on the Papeete waterfront, I had so little success at writing that my funds dwindled to the vanishing point. It seemed the part of wisdom to retire for a time to one of the remote country districts until I could repair my fortunes. On the southern side of the island, thirty-five miles from the town, I found a piece of land, an acre in extent, with a one-room house on it precisely suited to my needs. The veranda overlooked the sea, unbroken by any land as far as the Antarctic Circle, and a mountain stream flowed through my small domain so that I had both fresh-water and sea-water bathing. But a more important feature was the cheapness of the rental — three dollars per month.

The land thereabout was so fertile that I decided to make a vegetable garden. In the tropics gardening would be a delightful occupation, I thought, and it might prove so profitable that I would not need to attempt earning my living at my old trade of authorship. So I set to work hopefully enough, glad of the necessity which had brought me to this decision.

The experience was disillusioning. Millions of ants carried away most of my seed, and if any happened to be overlooked by the ants, the moment they sent forth green shoots these were sheared off by the land crabs. After months of patient effort, all that I had to show for my toil were a few ears of sweet corn — or, better, sweet corn cobs, for rats had eaten off the kernels — three small tomatoes and one squash. Having estimated my time as worth, at a modest figure, twenty cents an hour, and adding expenditures for seed, garden tools, and so on, I found that these vegetables cost me $15.50 each.

Nevertheless, I resolved to try once more and ordered — from America, this time — a small quantity of fresh seed, for my funds were low indeed, and, furthermore, because of my innumerable enemies I meant to garden on a reduced front. But when I had cleared away the weeds — how marvelously they had flourished meanwhile, without care! — and saw the hosts of ants drawn up in waiting battalions, and the ground perforated like a sieve with the holes of land crabs, with a crab at the entrance of each hole waving his keen-edged nippers in the air, I lost heart. "It is useless," I thought. "I'd better make another attempt at writing." It was not a lucrative profession, but if I practiced it faithfully I should be able to earn at least twenty cents an hour. Therefore, I put away my tools and let Nature plant whatever she would in my garden plot. She chose as before, lantana and a vicious weed called "false tobacco."

That afternoon as I was oiling and cleaning my typewriter which had long been rusting in disuse, a Chinese named Hop Sing drove past my door in his dilapidated spring wagon. He lived a quarter of a mile down the lagoon beach from my place, in a house he had built himself from the boards of old packing cases. I knew that he had a vegetable garden of sorts although he raised only sweet potatoes and a very tough variety of field corn; so I hailed him, thinking he might have use for my dollar's worth of seed. He stopped willingly enough, and I brought out to him a small packet each of beans, sweet corn (Golden Bantam), squash, pumpkin, lettuce and tomato seed, all of the best varieties. Sing grunted expressions of mild interest while I explained what the various packets contained, and when I had finished asked, "How much?" "Oh, nothing at all," I said. "It's a little present for you." He grasped the back of his seat to steady himself, perhaps, from the shock of receiving a present from a stranger, and his black eyes glittered a trifle more brightly, but these were the only evidences of emotion, if it may be called emotion, that he displayed.

I forgot Hop Sing forthwith. There were other things to think of, chiefly, the precarious state of my finances. Having counted upon my garden to furnish food I had spent my little capital all too freely. I had received in the meantime one check for twelve dollars and another for ten dollars in payment for some newspaper articles I had written earlier. Luckily my rent was paid several months in advance, but I had left only one hundred and twenty-eight francs — a little more than five dollars, American, at the current rate of exchange — and not another penny to be expected until I had written something: story, sketch, whatnot. The manuscript would have to be sent to America, my only market, and even though it should be accepted at once — a remote possibility — I could not hope to receive a check from such a distance for at least three months. How was I to live in the meantime? There were plenty of bananas on my place and about fifty coconut palms; but my landlord, a native, reserved the right to both the fruit and the nuts, which was no more than fair considering the modest rental he asked for house and grounds. He gathered the nuts as they fell and the bananas were picked green to send to the Papeete market. I thought of fishing, but remembering past experiences I knew it would be foolish to count on that. I had no better luck at fishing than I had at gardening. No, I would have to live, somehow, on my one hundred and twenty-eight francs. That, of course, was impossible, so I resolved not even to try. I kept twenty-eight francs for incidental expenses, spent twenty-five francs for native tobacco, and invested the remainder of my cash in sweet potatoes and tinned beef. When the food was gone — well, I would worry about that when the time came.

Three days later I was on page two of a sketch which I planned to call "Settling Down in Polynesia," a story of some experiences I had had the summer before. It was Sunday, but necessity knows no holy days and I was doing my utmost to work. But the mere fact of having to work seemed to make accomplishment impossible. I had written and rewritten the two pages of my story, trying with each new draft to blacken page three. I was aroused from a mood of profound dejection by a knock at the door.

It was Hop Sing, and with him were his wife, their three small children, and a wizened little man shaped like an interrogation point. Hop was dressed in a clean cotton undershirt and a pair of dungaree trousers. His wife wore a pyjama suit of black silk and her hair was elaborately dressed. She carried one child on her arm, led another by the hand, and the third, a baby, rode comfortably in a sling on her back. The children were beautifully dressed, and each of them wore a little skull-cap of blue silk, with flowers and butterflies embroidered on them with gold thread. The ancient wore a robe like a dressing gown. He was very feeble and got down from the wagon with difficulty. It was pathetic to see the effort it cost him to walk.

He would advance his staff a few inches, and, grasping it with both hands, make a shuffling hop up to it. Then he would rest for a moment while gathering strength for a new effort. We helped him up the steps, and at length all were seated on my back veranda, Mrs. Sing sitting sidewise in her chair because of the baby in the sling. My unwashed breakfast dishes were on the table, and several slices of fried sweet potatoes on a greasy plate looked anything but appetizing. I was ashamed of the disorder of the place, the more so because this was the first visit I'd ever had from the Sing family. Hop Sing and his wife looked around them in appraising fashion, but I could not judge from their faces what they thought of my house-keeping.

"My fadda-law," said Sing, indicating the old man.

I smiled and nodded.

A rather long silence followed. I felt embarrassed and could think of nothing to say.

"What name, you?" he then asked.

I told him. Another interval of silence. I gave my forefinger to the child on Mrs. Sing's lap. It clasped it gravely and held on. Mrs. Sing smiled. Her father, too, smiled; at least, his face wrinkled suddenly, like a pool into which several pebbles have been thrown. The baby in the sling was asleep, its chubby arms sticking straight out. It looked like a doll rather than a baby. The oldest child, a boy of six or seven, had the curious mature look and the air of precocious wisdom one often sees on the faces of Chinese children.

Sing took from his pocket one of the packets of seeds I had given him.

"What name, this?" he asked.

"In English? . . . Corn, sweet corn. Golden Bantam," I replied. "Very good. Tahiti corn no good — too tough. This corn fine."

"You get from Melica?"

I nodded. He brought forth the other packets. "All this Melican seed?"

It was, I said, and of the best varieties.

He was silent for a moment; then he said: "Make fine garden, now. Make plenty big tomato, plenty corn, plenty squash. Bimeby you see."

Thinking of my three tomatoes about the size of pigeon's eggs I was not sanguine about Hop Sing's being plenty big. However, I expressed the hope that they might be. I brought out a seed catalogue and showed him illustrations in color of various kinds of vegetables. The pictures, of course, showed products in their highest imaginative perfection. He was much interested and exchanged remarks in Chinese with his father-in-law. Meanwhile, one of those heavy showers common at Tahiti in the rainy season broke with violence. The thunder of water on my tin roof was deafening. Soon the cloud melted into pure sunlight, the last of it descending in a fine mist shot through with rainbow lights. Sing went out to his wagon and returned with three fine watermelons. He made a second excursion, bringing this time a live fowl, a bottle of Dubonnet (*vin apéritif*), and a basket containing seventeen eggs. All of these articles he placed on my kitchen table.

"Littly plesent, you," he said, with a deprecatory gesture. Mrs. Sing and her father then rose and all three shook my hand, bidding me good-by with smiles and nods. A moment later they drove off, leaving me astonished and genuinely moved at this expression of Chinese friendliness.

It would be difficult to exaggerate the value, to me, of their generous gift. Tinned beef is a nourishing food, but I had lost all relish for it during the First Great War. As for sweet potatoes, I had eaten so many while knocking about the Pacific on trading schooners that I could scarcely endure the sight of them. How welcome, then, was this more palatable food! I thought of having a chicken dinner at once, but on second thought decided to preserve my fowl. Perhaps she would lay, and if I could somehow procure a rooster I might from this small beginning raise enough chickens to provide for all my needs. So I staked the hen out in the dooryard with a string tied to her leg, and having found several coconuts partly eaten by rats, I broke these open and gave her a good meal. Then, having dined on a six-egg omelet with half a watermelon for dessert, I resumed my work with interest and enthusiasm. All the afternoon the bell of my typewriter rang with the steady persistence of an alarm gong at a railway crossing, and pages of manuscript fell on the floor around me like autumn leaves after a heavy frost. By six o'clock that evening I had reached the end of my "Settling Down" story.

I had no time to lose if I was to get it into the north-bound mail. The monthly steamer from New Zealand to San Francisco was due at Papeete on Monday. I decided to go into town to post the manuscript myself, not being willing to trust the native mail carrier with so precious a document. A motor bus ran daily between Papeete and Taravao, a village just beyond my place, but the fare for the round trip was twenty-four francs. I would need at least ten francs for stamps and expenses in town, so I decided to walk to Papeete, and if I had money enough left, to ride back. Having fortified myself with another six-egg omelet and a small glass of Dubonnet, I set out.

It was a beautiful night, dewy and still and fresh, with a full moon rising above the palm trees on the Taravao isthmus. The road wound around the shoulders of the hills, now skirting the sea, now crossing the mouths of broad valleys where the land breeze from the mountains blew cool and refreshing. I had glimpses through the trees of lofty precipices festooned with the silvery smoke of waterfalls, and, on the left hand, of the lagoon bordered by the reef, where great combers caught the moonlight in lines of white fire. From native houses along the road came snatches of song, a strange mixture of airs, part French, part Tahitian, to the accompaniment of guitars, accordions and mouth organs. On verandas here and there women were busy with their ironing, sitting cross-legged on the floor with a lamp beside them, and far out on the lagoon the lights of the fishermen were beginning to appear.

I walked briskly along the road, feeling at peace with the world and with myself. How pleasant, how wise it would be, I thought, really to settle down in this remote island paradise and remain here for the rest of my life. Where else could I find kindlier people, or a life more suited to one of my indolent habits? If it were true that a man's wealth may be estimated in terms of things he can do without, then in that sense I might hope soon to achieve affluence. Material possessions added little to the sum of one's happiness, and I could always earn enough at writing to provide for the simple necessities of life. Whenever the mild-eyed, melancholy tropical wolves came sniffing apologetically at my door, I could write a story of one sort or another, and live on the proceeds of the sale of it until it became necessary to write another.

Musing thus hopefully I proceeded on my way, but toward midnight when I had covered about half the distance to Papeete, I found myself again thinking of food. The nourishment stored in my second six-egg omelet had already been absorbed and its energy expended. I had a drink of water from a mountain stream and tightened my belt a notch or two. "I'll have a good breakfast when I reach town," I thought. For four francs I could buy a large portion of chop suey at one of the Chinese restaurants. That would suffice until I returned to the country, which I meant to do as soon as I had posted my manuscript.

At a place where the road followed a lonely strip of beach I came to a thatched hut, and sitting near it by a driftwood fire were an old native man and woman. I halted to enjoy the beauty of the scene. The stems of the coconut palms were black against the firelight, which flickered over the faces of the old couple and cast huge shadows behind them. They saw me and called out, "*Haere mai ta maa!*" (Come and eat!) This is merely a friendly greeting, and I replied in the customary way, "*Paia vau*" (I'm not hungry), but if my empty stomach could have spoken it would have made indignant denial of the statement. Evidently they really meant that I should partake of their midnight supper. They were roasting over the coals what appeared to be shellfish and some kind of native vegetable, and an appetizing fragrance filled the air.

"Come," said the old woman; "try this. It is very good," and, putting several generous portions in a coconut shell, she held it up to me.

Good? I should think it was! The meat of the shellfish was delicately flavored and the vegetable had real substance and a nutlike taste. My hosts were delighted to see the relish with which I ate and urged more food upon me.

"Eat, eat!" said the old man. "We have plenty, enough for a

dozen," and he pointed to several buckets filled with uncooked food. So, being very hungry, I ate with a will.

"What kind of shellfish are these?" I asked. "Did you catch them on the reef?"

"These are not shellfish. They're *tupas*," the old man said.

"What!" I exclaimed.

Tupas are land crabs, and those I had been eating with such relish were members of the pestiferous family, countless in numbers, which had assisted the ants in ruining my garden. I hadn't known they were edible, but my hosts told me that Tahitians thought them a great delicacy, which they are, in truth, if one is really hungry. As for the vegetable, it was not a vegetable at all, but a nut, the fruit of the *mapé*, the Pacific chestnut tree. These trees flourish on Tahiti. They are found along the banks of streams, and in other moist or swampy places. There was a grove of them on my place and the ground beneath was littered with nuts which my landlord never disturbed, and which I had not bothered to examine, not knowing they were good to eat.

I was appalled at thought of the time I had wasted trying to make a garden, when all the while there was an inexhaustible supply of food at hand, to be enjoyed without labor, to be had for the mere taking. But no, the taking of land crabs could not be such a simple matter. I remembered the wariness of those that infested my garden. They did all their damage in my absence. The moment they saw me they scurried to their holes and, if I made so much as a move in their direction, dodged down to safety. I had once caught one by digging him out, but that cost me half an hour of hard work.

I asked the old man how he caught them, and he showed me a method so simple and easy that I wondered I had not thought of it. He had a fishpole and line, but instead of a hook at the end of the line, he tied there a bunch of green leaves from the hibiscus tree. These leaves and the blossoms of the hibiscus are the principal food of land crabs when there is no garden stuff at hand. We went a little way from the hut to a spot in full moonlight where there were many crab holes. "Now stand very still," he said. In a moment the crabs, which had vanished at our approach, came warily up again. He then cast his bait much as one does in fly-fishing. The crabs fastened their nippers in the leaves, each of them trying to drag the bundle to his hole. The old man gave the line a deft jerk, and the crabs, not being able to disengage their nippers quickly enough, were dragged to his feet. He pounced upon them and threw them into the bucket with the others.

I then tried my hand, with such success that I was tempted to return home at once and begin fishing in my garden. But more prudent counsels prevailed. One's appetite for food so plentiful and so easily procured might become jaded in time. Furthermore I would need a certain amount of money for paper, typewriter ribbons, shaving materials, and such. So I bade farewell to my friendly hosts and proceeded on my way, reaching Papeete at dawn, just as the steamer which was to carry my manuscript to America was entering the harbor. Stamps for the parcel cost three francs. I breathed over it a silent prayer and slipped it into the letter chute.

I have heard travelers call Papeete a tropical slum, and it must be admitted that it does leave something to be desired in the way of cleanliness and sanitation. Nevertheless it is a colorful town, particularly in the early morning when the people are going to and from the market place. Everyone is abroad at that hour and the French and Chinese restaurants are filled with folk exchanging gossip over their morning coffee. I had a good breakfast at the cost of four francs, then strolled along the waterfront, doubly enjoying the gaiety of the scene after my long sojourn in the country. I was walking along the Quai de Commerce looking at the shipping when someone touched my shoulder. It was a bald, fat little Chinese who had evidently been running after me. He was so out of breath that he could not speak for a moment. Then he began talking in Chinese-Tahitian, a sort of *biche-la-mer* I don't understand. I shook my head. He renewed his efforts, speaking earnestly and rapidly, and I caught the name Hop Sing.

"Hop Sing?" I said.

"*É! É!*" (Yes! Yes!) he replied, and of a sudden found some English words.

"You know Hop Sing? Hop Sing flen, you?"

Yes, I said, I knew him. "Hop Sing live close me, Papéari."

Papéari was the name of the district where I was living.

The face of the Chinese glowed with pleasure.

"*Maitai, maitai!*" (Good!) "Hop Sing send me letta. I know name, you! You give seed, put in gloun, make garden. *Maitai! Maitai!* Hop Sing glad. Me glad. Hop Sing bruddalaw, me."

"What name, you?" I asked.

"Lee Fat. Keep store, over there," and he pointed down the street. "When you go back Papéari?"

"Go this morning, on motor bus," I replied.

"Goo-by," said the Chinese, and rushed away without another word. I was surprised at the abrupt leave-taking and stood looking after him, touched at the thought of this odd little man chasing me down the street to thank me for the trifling favor I had done his brother-in-law.

I sat on the bench near the post office to wait for the motor bus. "The beachcombers' bench," it was called, for it was usually occupied on steamer day with waifs and strays from various parts of the world who sit there waiting for the distribution of the monthly mail, always expecting letters containing money and nearly always disappointed. "I'm in the same boat now," I thought. "Three months hence I'll be sitting here nursing the same forlorn hope." It was possible, of course, that my manuscript would sell at once, but repeated past experience warned me that it would be foolish to count on it. Well, I still had twenty-one francs and would have nine left after paying my bus fare. Certainly, I would not starve, with land crabs and *mapé* nuts to eat. Meanwhile I would work as never before, sending out manuscripts as long as I could find money for postage. Having made this resolve I put my worries aside.

It was nearly midday when I arrived at Papéari. While paying the driver my fare, the boy who attended to the distribution of parcels put a box down beside me.

"You've made a mistake," I said. "That isn't mine."

"Yes it is," he replied.

"No, no. I didn't have a box and I've ordered nothing from town."

He insisted, however, that it was mine. A Chinese had brought it just before the bus left the market, he said, and had paid for its carriage to my place. I still thought there was some mistake, but upon prying off the lid I found a card with "Lee Fat. No. 118" printed on it. Every Chinese on Tahiti has a number, for identification purposes. Under the name was written, in pencil: "Mr. Hall, for you."

The parcel contained the following articles: a two-pound box of New Zealand chocolates, a paper bag of litchi nuts, one quart of champagne (Louis Roederer), and a Chinese lacquered box with a gold dragon on the lid. In the box were two silk handkerchiefs and a silk pyjama suit.

I was tempted to open the champagne at once that I might drink long life and abundant health to Hop Sing and his brother-in-law, Lee Fat, No. 118; but I had no ice, and I knew that I could not drink a quart of champagne without having a headache, afterward. So I tied a string to the bottle and lowered it into the cistern, to cool. Then I went out to attend to my hen.

She was gone. The string was still tied to the stake, but she had worked her foot out of the noose and vanished. After a long search I found her under the back steps. She had laid an egg and was sitting on it. Evidently she was ready to set when Hop Sing brought her to me. The egg under her was probably unfertilized so I took that out. Then I made her a nest of the excelsior which had been packed around the articles in Lee Fat's gift box, and placed in it the five eggs remaining from Hop Sing's gift. The hen settled down upon them with contented cluckings, and when comfortable closed her eyes as much as to say: "Now then, all I ask is to be left alone, and twenty-one days hence we shall see what we shall see."

It seems to me now that the definite upward trend in the graph of my fortunes began that afternoon when I started land-crab fishing. I could not eat a tenth of the crabs I caught, so I made a pen of stakes set closely together and driven deeply into the ground, and turned the surplus loose inside it.

They immediately dug new holes for themselves, but this did not disturb me, for I knew that I could easily catch them again. It occurred to me that by feeding them regularly on hibiscus leaves and blossoms I might add to their size and increase the delicacy of their flavor. The experiment was highly successful. The crabs throve upon regular and abundant food and I throve upon them. At the time of Hop Sing's visit, what with worry and an uncongenial diet, I was very thin, but within six weeks I had gained fourteen pounds.

Meanwhile, promptly upon the appointed day, my hen stepped out of her nest followed by four chicks. I was quite as proud of them as she was and doubtless took more credit to myself on the occasion than the facts warranted. I fed the hen and her brood on a mixture of roasted land crabs and ground *mapé* nuts, and never have I seen baby chicks grow more rapidly.

It may seem incredible that my bottle of champagne should have remained unbroached during this time, but such is the case. In my interest in crab-and-chicken farming I had quite forgotten it; but one day when my landlord was gathering coconuts in a nearby grove I invited him in to share it with me. He was more than willing, and his somewhat reserved attitude toward me altered with the first glass. I then learned the reason for his coolness. He told me that his last tenant had not only eaten bananas and coconuts to which he had no right, but had gone away without paying his rent, three months in arrears at that time. Gathering, from the simplicity of my way of life, that I too had little money, he feared that I might play him the same trick. I reassured him on this point and we drank confusion to his former tenant, wherever he might be. Several of my landlord's children had accompanied him to the house and I shared among them the box of chocolates. It was a merry little party, and after much pleasant talk my landlord left me with repeated expressions of good will.

The next morning I found on my back veranda a bunch of bananas and a copra sack half filled with mangoes and oranges, gifts from my landlord and his family. Not infrequently, thereafter, Mata, his wife, would send me baked fish, breadfruit, and mountain plantain, fresh from her native oven, and I remembered with deep gratitude that I really owed these benefits to Hop Sing.

Meanwhile, I worked steadily at writing and Hop Sing's garden was flourishing. All the seeds I had given him had sprouted and gave promise of a rich harvest under his patient, ceaseless care. He was always at work and so too was Mrs. Sing, despite the demands on her time made by three small children. Sometimes of a late afternoon I walked down to their place. They always greeted me in the most friendly way, but never for a moment did they leave off working. "Surely," I would think, "the Chinese deserve to inherit the earth, and doubtless will inherit it if industry and patience count for anything." Even the ancient, not Mrs. Sing's father but her grandfather, as I was to learn, was far from being useless, despite his little strength; and the oldest child, although only a baby himself, took care of his smaller brother. Mrs. Sing was usually to be found in a little back shed sorting and cleaning vegetables for the Papeete market. All of her members were busy at once. She rocked the smallest baby, which lay in a little cradle hanging from a rafter, by means of a cord attached to her foot. Now and then she pulled another cord which hung just over her head. This one ran by a system of pulleys to the garden where there was a sort of jumping-jack scarecrow to frighten away those robbers, the mynah birds. Meanwhile, the vegetables got themselves cleaned and deftly packed in little baskets.

The ancient was a baker and twice a week, after his long day's toil in the garden, Hop Sing made the rounds of the district in his spring wagon, selling crisp loaves of bread and pineapple tarts to the native population. During these excursions he often left something at my gate, either a tart or a loaf of bread. No protest on my part served to dry up his fountain of gratitude for my wretched little gift of seed.

Under these circumstances the weeks passed so pleasantly that steamer day — the third since the posting of my manuscript — was at hand before I realized it. I walked into town once more and waited on the familiar bench till the mail should be distributed. I waited through the latter part of the afternoon until everybody in Papeete and its environs had called for their letters. I waited until the sun was sinking behind the mountains of Moorea and the post office was about to close. Then, summoning all my resolution, I mounted the steps and walked to the delivery window, saying inwardly: "It's useless to ask. I'm quite certain to be disappointed." The girl who presided there went hastily through a small number of letters from the "H" box.

"No, there's nothing for you," she said, with a smile so typical of post-office clerks who preside at General Delivery windows.

I made a ghastly attempt to smile in return and was going toward the door when she called after me:

"Oh! Just a moment! What name did you say?"

I repeated it, enunciating the words with the utmost care.

"Yes, there is one letter," she said. "Fifty centimes postage due."

Having paid this I had left only a twenty-five-centime piece, the smallest coin used in French Oceania. But little that mattered. The letter contained a gracious note accepting my manuscript, and a check for five hundred dollars.

To those living luxurious lives in the high latitudes, five hundred dollars may seem a trifling sum, but it was a fortune to me. I had never before received even a half of that amount for anything I had written. With the half of it, plus two dollars, I could pay the rental for my house and grounds for a period of seven years, and the two hundred and fifty remaining would suffice for other expenses for a time nearly as long, provided that I lived as modestly in the future as I had in the immediate past. But now, with bright vistas of ease and plenty and peace of mind opening out before me, I found myself perversely considering the idea of leaving Tahiti. The north-bound steamer to San Francisco would be due shortly, and I fell to considering the varied experience I might now have by virtue of movement and my five hundred dollars. Remembering past fortunes in authorship, I knew that it was the part of wisdom to remain on Tahiti where living was, for the first time, within my means. And yet, if I did not go now, I might have to wait long before I should again have enough money for a steamship ticket. I walked the streets of Papeete until a late hour, anxiously considering this matter. The clock in the cathedral was striking two before the decision — to go — was made.

Hop Sing was in town on the day of my departure. He had come with garden produce, and both he and Lee Fat came to see me off. Fat insisted on my accepting a pair of Russia-

leather bedroom slippers and a Chinese fan of blue silk em-
bellished with gold butterflies hovering over a fantasy of
flowers. Sing's parting gift was a basket of tomatoes as large
as oranges, and a dozen ears of sweet corn (Golden Bantam).
They smiled good-bys as the steamer backed away from the
wharf and headed for the passage to the open sea. I then
went to my cabin, in order that departure from that most
beautiful of islands might be a little less poignant. While I
was unpacking my bag, a steward looked in.

"You've been assigned to the doctor's table, sir," he said.
"It's a table for four, but this trip there's only one other
gentleman there beside yourself. Is that satisfactory?"

"Quite," I replied. "By the way, will you please have this
corn prepared and served at luncheon? Take a couple of ears
for yourself if you care to."

"Thank you, sir. I hope the other gentleman at your table
likes sweet corn. He's done nothing but complain about the
food ever since we left Wellington, and to tell you the truth,
it's not what it might be."

The doctor did not come down for luncheon. I had just
seated myself when the other passenger at his table came in.
He was a tall, spare man with a drooping mustache and a
bilious complexion. He was dressed in a baggy linen coat
and knickerbockers and low white shoes. He sat down without even a nod in my direction and adjusted a pair of nose
glasses, picking up the menu card, puffing out his cheeks as
he examined it, letting the air escape dejectedly through
his lips. He struck me as being a man who would be extremely
hard to please in the matter of food or anything else. He
was partaking gloomily of a dish of creamed tinned salmon
when the steward brought in a platter with eight splendid

ears of Golden Bantam corn steaming on it. He gazed at it in astonishment.

"Take this away," he said to the steward, pushing the dish of salmon to one side, "and bring me another dinner plate."

Never before had I seen a man give himself up to the enjoyment of food with such purely physical abandon. One would have thought he had not eaten for days. When he had finished his second ear he said: "Steward, where does this corn come from? It's not on the card."

"No, sir, it's not on the regular bill. It's a gift to the table from the gentleman sitting opposite you."

He gave me a grudging glance as though he had just become aware of my presence.

"Consider yourself thanked, sir," he said, brusquely.

I nodded.

"Is this corn of your own growing?"

"Well, yes, in a sense," I replied.

He plowed a hasty furrow along his third ear before speaking again. Then he said: "What do you mean by 'in a sense'? You either raised it or you didn't, I should think."

He had a waspish, peppery way of speaking as though he had been long accustomed to asking whomever, whatever he chose, with the certainty of a deferential reply. In view of the fact that he was eating my — or rather, Hop Sing's — corn, I felt that he might have made an effort, at least, to be gracious. Therefore I merely said, as coldly as possible, "Oh, you'd have to live on Tahiti to understand that." Having finished my luncheon I rose and left him there, still eating corn.

Half an hour later I was standing at the rail, aft, watching the peak of Orofena, the highest mountain on Tahiti, slowly sinking into the sea. A hand was laid on my arm, and, turning, I found my table companion.

"Well, sir," he said, "one would think that you were about to jump overboard."

"I have been considering it," I replied; "but it's too far to swim back, now."

"You like Tahiti as much as that? Well, I don't wonder. An island where they grow such delicious corn must be a good place to live. I ate six of those ears — finished the lot, in fact."

"I'm glad you enjoyed it," I replied.

"See here! You mustn't mind my grumpiness. I'm afraid I was a little brusque at luncheon. I've got dyspepsia, and a wayward liver and an enlarged spleen — Lord knows what-all else the matter with me. Gives me a sort of jaundiced outlook on life. But I want you to know that I'm grateful. Sweet corn is one of the few things I can eat without suffering afterward. Now, then, tell me something about your island. I didn't go ashore. Useless trying to see even a small island in six hours. It's only an aggravation."

I scarcely know how it came about, but within a few minutes I was talking as freely as though to an old friend. I told him of the beauty of the islands in the eastern Pacific, of the changing life, of the mingling races; of the strange outcroppings of savage beliefs and customs through the shale of what in those parts is called civilization. Presently I halted, thinking he might be bored.

"Not at all," he said. "Well, you've had an interesting time, evidently, and you seem to have made good use of your eyes and ears. You're an American, aren't you? What do you do for a living — besides raising sweet corn, 'in a sense'?" he added, with a smile.

I told him that I was an itinerant journalist.

"Is that so?" he said, looking interested. "Got any of your stuff with you?"

"A few sketches of various sorts," I replied.

"Would you mind letting me see them?"

"Not in the least." And so, at his suggestion I brought out a small sheaf of manuscript, six slight papers on various island subjects, each of them about two thousand words long. He settled himself in his deck chair and adjusted his glasses.

"Come back an hour from now," he said, "and I'll tell you what I think of them."

He thought two of them worthless, and, strangely enough, they were the ones I thought best.

"But these four are not bad. What do you want for them?"

"You . . . you mean you would like to buy them?" I asked.

"Yes, of course. But I forgot to tell you: I'm the director of a newspaper syndicate in the U.S.A. We can use these sketches. Tropical island stuff is always popular. Interest in the South Seas never wanes, and it never will as long as life is what it is in America. . . . Well, what do you want for them?"

"Oh, I don't know . . ." I said. I was about to add: "Would one hundred dollars be too much?" meaning one hundred for the four. He interrupted me.

"Give you one hundred and fifty each for them. Is that agreeable?"

I admitted that it was.

That evening I set down on paper, for my own amusement, a list as complete as I could make it of all the benefits, direct and indirect, accruing to me from my trifling gift to Hop Sing. With this before me I came to the conclusion that Adam himself, the first husbandman, even under the exceptionally favorable conditions prevailing in the Garden of Eden before the Fall, could not have reaped such a rich and varied harvest as I did from my garden at Tahiti. And it all came from a dollar's worth of seed.

IV. A Happy Hedonist

THERE IS A BOOK in my library which I have read three or
four times during the past twenty-five years and which holds
my interest today fully as much as when I first read it shortly
after its publication, in 1923. It is called *Isles of Illusion*,
and comprises a series of letters written from the South Seas
during the years 1912–1920, by an Englishman to an English friend and former Oxford classmate, at home. Most of
them are dated from various islands in the New Hebrides
archipelago; a few at the close of the volume were written
from an island in French Polynesia. The name of the man
who wrote them is not given. He is called, merely, "Asterisk."
That they are genuine there can be no slightest doubt in the
mind of anyone who has read them.

What makes them so interesting to me is the picture they
give of an intelligent, sensitive, fastidious man, without
money, thrown upon his own resources in a primitive tropical environment. He was disgusted with modern life, modern civilization. He was sick and tired of England — he wanted
to be happy and he found no happiness there. He wanted
to be free to live his life in his own way, largely outside the
conventions of gregarious folk. And so, with some misgivings

and with many sanguine hopes, he set out in search of this freedom.

Of his life previous to the New Hebrides experience we know the little that his friend, who published the letters, tells in a brief introduction. His father, the product of an old-time grammar school, taught him Latin when he was five. He was then sent to a Wesleyan school and from there to "a local preparatory school for the sons of gentlemen." Various other schools followed, and in his seventeenth year he went to London to be enrolled as a medical student. He had been given a lump sum which was to have kept him and paid his fees until he qualified. This he spent, apparently, for other things than fees. Then his father died, and with his money gone there was no more medical school, but by that time he had a groundwork in medicine that was to stand him in good stead, later. He became a bank clerk and afterward there was a long period of teaching as junior master in a preparatory school. A legacy received in his twenty-ninth year enabled him to go to Oxford where his pride suffered because he was compelled to associate with men seven or eight years his junior. His friend says that "he took a fairly tolerable place in the Chemistry School; and so to the peak of his ambition at last — a mastership at a public school." After teaching in England for some two years he rebelled and went to South America where followed another period of usherdom and disgust. It was from Montevideo that he set out for the South Seas.

Robert Louis Stevenson's books first turned his thoughts toward the Pacific. What a great amount of disillusionment in other men Stevenson has, quite innocently, to answer for! I have read all of his South Sea books, both descriptive and imaginative, and I cannot find that he painted life in the islands in such rosy colors. There was a deal of glamour, of course, in what he wrote of them: Stevenson found glamour wherever he went; and the result was that a small army of men, most of them young, some of them middle-aged, and a few old in years but still young in hope, followed him in his wanderings, particularly to the Pacific in search of the Delectable Isles. Individuals here and there have found them, but Asterisk was not among the number. There were times when he thought he had — moments when he was radiantly certain that he had. But always afterward came the reaction: he loathed with an intense and bitter hatred everything connected with the South Seas. It was the old story of a man trying to find the material counterpart of a dream. It was the old story, too, of a man carrying his own little private hell, himself, with him wherever he went, fondly hoping that a mere change of scene would, somehow, transform it into a miniature Garden of Eden.

His choice of the New Hebrides was, to say the least, unfortunate. Had he searched the Pacific over he could hardly have found a group of islands less suited as places for white men to live. As a matter of fact he did not deliberately choose this group. An opportunity for going to New Caledonia came to him while he was schoolmastering in Montevideo, and as it was a move in the right direction he decided to take it. He went with another Englishman who had partially persuaded him that they could make their fortunes as planters in the South Seas. Asterisk had no desire to make a fortune; all he wanted was enough money to insure independence, and he was willing to sacrifice ten years of his life, if necessary, to the Mammon of Business in order to lay by a small competence. In one of his early letters to his friend in England, written on shipboard during the twelve-thousand-mile voyage to New Caledonia, he says:

> Brookes pesters me to death with elaborate figures concerning plantations and I pretend to be interested. I suppose we shall be successful but I don't seem to care. Sometimes I wish I had waited and gone in my own way to do what I wanted. But then I think that the time might never have come. . . . Brookes reckons that in about ten years we ought to be making about £2000 a year. Then he is going to retire and live comfortably in England. Shall I have lost my faculty of appreciation by then? I don't think so. I am going to treat my inner self most carefully all the time, so as to husband all of my strength, all my longing and love of beauty, and I really hope that instead of having deteriorated it will have increased tremendously.

One would say that this letter had been written by a young man; it breathes the very spirit of youth, and yet at this time Asterisk must have been in his late thirties. One reason why I find his letters so interesting is that they seem to be the expression of two men: one of them young, naïve, full of illusions; the other old and bitter and cynical.

But it seems that his friend, Brookes, had made a mistake in his arithmetic, "a nought too few or too many or something." When they arrived at Nouméa, in New Caledonia, they found that their planters' project was no better than a pipe dream. The gains were slow and very uncertain; furthermore, a large capital was necessary and they had barely enough money to pay their living expenses for a week. "So back to the hotel to reconstruct our plans. Brookes immediately cabled his brother, in Japan, is off there, via Sydney, on the 20th. I found myself left stranded, a waif in the great Pacific."

Asterisk made no appeals to relatives or friends but set out to look for a job. He found one as a plantation manager in the New Hebrides at six pounds per month, all found.

> Needless to say I have already determined to accept. I have learned much about the New Hebrides. From all accounts they are worthy, very worthy from the point of view of beauty, typical South Sea Islands of the stuff of which we have dreamed. There is a drawback, malaria . . . but I am not afraid because the risks are enormously lessened by proper care and a decent physique. Of course, if I find that it makes life impossible I shall move on.

He did find that malaria made life all but impossible, but he did not move on. He remained in the New Hebrides for seven and a half years.

Solitude closed in upon him at once. You all but see it flowing around him silently and smoothly, as though it were something tangible like water. I have often wondered why it is that tropical solitude seems harder to bear than that of the unfrequented places of the north. A gray, misty, northern sea with never a sail on it is nothing like so lonely as a tropical sea, bright and blue and sparkling in the afternoon sunshine. As for landscape, go to the bleakest, the most barren of northern lands, and you do not have there the feeling of forsakenness which often assails you in tropical countries where Nature is so exuberantly lovely, so smilingly indifferent to your little concerns and worries. The wan sunlight of the north has in it something consoling and friendly and the sky seems not so far away. In the tropics it is otherwise. There, "high noon" is a fearfully expressive term. High it is, in all truth — high beyond the farthest reach of fancy. A brief, bewildered, groping glance toward that infinity of blue brings home to you, not intellectually as in the north, but emotionally, what an atom of dust you are, creeping under that brilliant sky. And when you seek escape from this overwhelming sense of littleness by going into the depths of some valley, the damp sepulchral gloom and the utter silence soon drive you forth again. Yes, assuredly, one finds solitude at its worst in the tropics.

In Asterisk's case it was not so much purely physical isolation. Often there were other human beings within reach, but with a few exceptions he preferred unbroken solitude to their companionship. His was a spiritual and intellectual isolation and one marvels that he endured it for seven and a half years. Probably he could not have endured it had it not been for his friend in England. One is glad that he had such a friend to turn to. He poured out his soul to him, told him all that he was doing, thinking, hoping, suffering. He sent him voluminous letters at every opportunity. That his friend was a true friend in need is evident from the following:

> If ever a man deserved salvation for a single act, you do for the writing of the letter which I received yesterday. I was feeling miserable, sitting at my tent door in the cool of the evening, gnawing my nails and cursing everything, looking out to sea with no hope of seeing even a canoe. In the failing light I saw a speck, a lump on the water, an excrescence, mast and no sails. It must be a launch. It must be Bernhardt, because no one else ventures up this wild coast. I got up and ran a good mile to where I knew he must anchor, and got there as he

came ashore in his dinghy. He had got my mail, a great
fat parcel of it. Incidentally he had got my tobacco and I
had been smoking "trade" for a week — and there sticking out in the most obtrusive manner was your letter.
I shook Bernhardt warmly by the hand (he thought I
was drunk, as he was) and ran back to my tent. I had to
be alone. I felt the envelope and it was so thick, and then
(don't laugh!) I kissed it. . . . I opened and read sol-
emnly and conscientiously my other letters — dull non-
sense about surveying from lawyers. Then I mixed myself
a mighty pipe of Baron, mixed a corresponding whiskey
and started to read.

One likes to think that he had this pleasure often, and
only lonely men who live in the backwaters of the world
know what a pleasure it is. No doubt he did have it, although
he sometimes reproaches his friend for sending him skimpy
letters. But it must be remembered that his friend was living in England, in wartime. It would not be surprising if he
sometimes forgot or temporarily neglected "the happy hedon-
ist," as Asterisk bitterly styled himself in one of his letters.

He has much to say of loneliness, and gives some vivid
and memorable descriptions of his reactions to it. The solitude
of the spirit which all sensitive men feel at times, wherever
they may be, was objectified for him. It was like a presence.
It seemed to take on a shadowy substance and to follow him
wherever he went.

I fill my day as far as ever I can with the, to me,
peculiarly obnoxious details of plantation life. But always
there is the horror beside me, saying, "When there is
nothing more to do, or when you are tired, you will have
no one to speak to. There will be nothing new, nothing

new anywhere." I rush out and stare at the sea and the horizon. I know every detail of it by heart. I know there will never be a sail to break that ghastly line. And yet I stare and stare. . . . It is the knowledge that one is "right up against it" that is so appalling; that one is bound to go on living this rat's existence for months if not years to come.

There were years of it to come, and as the New Hebrides are pestilential places, particularly during the rainy season, Asterisk suffered all the ills that tropical flesh is heir to, with the exception of blackwater fever. A large part of the time he was dopey with quinine. He drank much whiskey, partly for health's sake, partly to make solitude more endurable. Weakened as he was by recurring attacks of fever, sitting in his little "iron hell" drenched with perspiration, tormented by swarms of flies, fleas and mosquitoes, sick at heart and often too utterly weary to read, his thoughts went round in a circle with himself perpetually in the center.

His opinions of places varied considerably, depending upon whether he was ill or comparatively well when he set them down; but his opinions of his fellow colonials changed little from first to last. With a few notable exceptions he hated them. They were largely responsible for the great amount of bile he discharged into his letters. In doing so he gained momentary relief, but there was always more and to spare where that came from. The Australians were his particular abominations. He called them "Orstrylyuns," imitating their own pronunciation. He loathed them individually and collectively. He hated their phonographs with their cheap music-hall records, and their practice of invading his privacy of a Sunday, bringing their "phono" with them. And then, instead of talking on paper with his friend in England, he would be compelled to listen to the kind of music which enchanted them. "'Ere, chum, lissen to this." The mechanism is set going, and Asterisk, "the savourer of pleasureable emotions," hears a Sydney vaudeville artist, singing:

> 'Old yer 'and out, naughty boy!
> 'Old yer 'and out, naughty boy!

He hated their accent, their obscenity, their boastful talk of "woyte Orstrylia for woyte Orstryliuns," their perpetual "nigger-cheating," and their shameless brutality to these same black islanders.

> . . . the treatment of these poor wretches makes me writhe. People howl about Chinese slavery. I could tell them things about the recruiting and treatment of kanakas that would open their eyes a bit. . . . They are enticed away by every species of trickery, often by actual violence, and then the gold-greedy white man wonders that they don't toil for twelve hours in blazing sun with one meal of rice, willingly and heartily that "master" may become rich.
>
> I feel almost at the end of my tether and can't stand this crowd of Commonwealth yobs any longer. Their conceit is insufferable, their ignorance is unplumbable. I can't even understand their language. Could you feel interested in a "bosker come-back"? Would you, at my age, like to be called a "Jackeroo"? . . . The English words that strike my ear are chiefly: blahdy, boi cripes, petreotism, Kichnur, and the boieys.

He acknowledges on another occasion that they are not all so bad as he has painted them, and he wonders whether he is not a degenerate and a snob because he dislikes their company and finds that he has nothing in common with them.

It would be strange if, during a period of nearly eight years, he never had a really happy day. He did have some, but they were few and far between, and one seems to catch the light from them long afterward, through the gloom of succeeding days. Meanwhile he was doing all sorts of things to make a living. At first he managed plantations. Then, because of his knowledge of languages — he both read and spoke French, Italian and Spanish — he was offered, and accepted, a position as interpreter-translator at the High Court at Vila. The New Hebrides, it may be well to explain, are held jointly by England and France and governed by a joint Commission. The work here was confining and he suffered much from fever, but as usual, it was the people rather than the work and the illness that he couldn't stand. The society of the little tropical port was not at all to his taste, so he held himself aloof. What he disliked particularly was that in his subordinate position as court interpreter he had to be both respectable and respectful.

I have to bow and smirk and say, "Parfaitement, Monsieur le Président." "Je vous serai infiniment obligé, Monsieur le Procureur," etc., when what I would like to say would not bear writing. I am longing to be free to do, say, wear and think what I damn well please. I didn't leave usherdom to become a *rond de cuir,* and that is what I shall speedily become here if I don't die or go mad first. Why should I be the slave of other people's convention, their paltry laws and accursed consciences? My life is all my own to play with and experiment with just as it seems good to me. I know that this is foolish and very largely impossible, but I intend to have my times of freedom, if only to chortle about them when I return to live among folk who dare not form an opinion for themselves, let alone perform an independent act.

It is hard to think of Asterisk as having been a schoolmaster, or as having wanted to be one. He seems to have been a born hater of conventional life, a born kicker against the pricks. Nevertheless, I venture to say that he was a first-rate master who did his work conscientiously and well, bitterly though he may have hated methods of teaching and all the rest of it. It is plain from his letters that he was a man who took pride in his work whether he liked it or not, and tried always to give the best of himself to whatever he was doing. But it is remarkable that he remained a teacher for so long. He really did believe in personal freedom. He really did believe that his life was his own to experiment with as he chose. At length he decided upon an experiment which was a dangerous one, to say the least. He took a native "wife," in the island fashion.

This was in the fourth year of his sojourn, and three years after his experience as court interpreter In the meantime, having traveled all over the archipelago as a surveyor, he had again become a plantation manager. Evidently, his attitude toward the natives had undergone a change during these years. In 1914 he tells his friend that the New Hebrides kanaka is the last word in ugliness, filth and depravity, and the fact of a white man mating with a female of such a kind argues even greater depravity, and shocking bad taste "even on the part of an Orstrylyun." Two years later, in announcing his decision, he explains to his friend that his wife, although a New Hebridean, comes from the island of Aoba, and that the Aobans are freaks among the natives, being Malayan rather than Papuan.

Their complexion is light; their hair yellowish and long; their features are good. I should not call the women classically beautiful, but they are very pleasant and petite. Also they are worshippers of bodily cleanliness, spending the whole day in the sea.

From this time on his letters are of the greatest interest, for Asterisk tried to be, and usually succeeded in being, quite honest with himself. I believe that his conventional self was convinced, almost at once, that he had gotten into a mess; but you see his unconventional self looking at the matter from every possible angle, trying to decide whether, viewed broadly, it was really a mess or not. The latter rarely had the upper hand in the argument. Asterisk realized that he was treading a dangerous path, but despite his misgivings he got a great deal of amusement out of his "experiment," and one can imagine him thinking, "I wish that some of my school-mastering colleagues could look in on me now. Wouldn't they be horrified!" He taught "Topsy," as he called her, *biche-la-mer*, and tried to learn her own island dialect. Solitude was more supportable now, and sometimes, particularly when she was ill, he realized with something of a shock "how absurdly and disgustingly attached" he had grown to his little brown woman, who sat on the floor and sang little songs, behaving toward him just as a nice Persian kitten would behave.

Sometimes I have the ordinary futile longing for a soul mate, for the wife who could be all in all to me . . . for the intellectual life *à deux*. More often now I understand that I am better off with my nut-brown savage who, two

minutes after a storm of tears . . . was choking with
laughter over "Simon says thumbs up." "*Allez!* Go on
again! Me want win 'im, you." She will play for hours at
these nursery games. Do you remember playing pat-a-
cake with your nurse? Topsy loves it. Many a time when
I have been aching for sleep she has kept me up with,
"'e no long time sleep yet. *Allez!* You me, two."

Thank heaven I can still howl with laughter and forget
my age and pomposity on suitable occasions. I trust I
shall never develop a sense of the fitness of things. One
is always fit to be a fool, no matter what young fools
may think.

If I could come to Europe, pick my woman, and be
free and independent to raise my kids in my own way,
there would be something over which to hesitate. But
the alternative is denied me. What woman — except such
an one as I should loathe — would marry me, middle-
aged, penniless, bald, ugly and cranky? I have not got
— and I thank my own god for it — one feature that
would redeem me in the eyes of such a bourgeoise as
I could marry.

It was at about this time that his friend in England had rec-
ommended his reading some Henry James. It was a curious
suggestion under the circumstances, and Asterisk confessed,
emphatically and picturesquely, that it did not appeal to him.
There is no doubt in my own mind, either, that Henry James
is not the novelist for a man living in wild country, more particularly in wild tropical country. I once tried reading *The
Awkward Age* on an atoll in the Low Archipelago. It was a
beautiful island; the palms were always bending to the cool
trade wind, blowing across hundreds of leagues of lonely sea.
I was tranquil in mind, healthy in body, and free from inter-

ruptions of any sort. And yet I couldn't read *The Awkward Age*. All I got from my attempt was a sense of the unreality of polite civilized life, and of the art, however admirable, that dealt with it. I can understand Asterisk's lack of appreciation in the stifling pestilential heat of the New Hebrides.

It is interesting to speculate as to what Henry James would have made of life in such a place had he gone there at Asterisk's age, or perhaps a little earlier. I have said that Asterisk was a fastidious man — and so he was, despite the nonfastidious things he did — but Henry James was a thousand times more so. What would have happened to him had he been compelled to remain in such an archipelago for ten or fifteen years, say — to work for a living and to live alone without intellectual companionship? But this is altogether too farfetched a speculation. Henry James would never have gone in the first place. The nearest one could come to a parallel case is, I think, that of Henry Adams who, in the early eighteen-nineties, with his friend John La Farge, made a voyage across the Pacific, stopping at Hawaii, Samoa, Tahiti, Fiji and elsewhere. Adams, of course, had ample funds, could move about as he pleased and procure such comforts as the islands afforded. But if ever there was a man unhappy and out of place in the South Seas, it was, surely, he. In a letter dated March 16, 1891, and written from Tautira, one of the outlying districts on the island of Tahiti, he wrote:

> I am bored — oh great Taaroa, known in Samoa as Tangaloa, how I am bored! Never have I known what it was to be bored before, even in the worst wilds of Beacon Street or at the dreariest dinner-tables of Belgravia. My mind has given way. I have horrors. No human being ever saw life more lovely than here, and I

actually sit, hour after hour, doing nothing but look out at the sea and sky because it is exquisitely lovely and makes me so desperately homesick; and I cannot understand either why it is so beautiful or why it makes me so frantic to escape. We have not seen a human being except villagers whom we cannot talk with. In desperation at sitting still, I try to paint, and the painting seems more futile than the sitting still. We have read all the works in Tahiti, and as for me, I am so tired of reading about the virtues and vices of the Tahitians that I wish I could see some. As for the Tahitians that have come within my acquaintance, except when they happened to be Jews, they have been the most commonplace, dreary, spiritless people I have yet seen. If they have amusements or pleasures, they conceal them. Neither dance nor game have I seen or heard of; nor surf-swimming nor ball-playing nor anything but the stupid mechanical *himene*. They do not even move with spirit. If I were not afraid of extravagance I should say that they were more melancholy than Hawaiians.

To come back to Asterisk, not many records, however intimate, throw such a revealing light into a man's mind and heart as these letters of his do. You see every corner of both as clearly as you see his lonely figure going resolutely about his work; or sitting under a tree, thinking things over, pipe in mouth, his battered old sun helmet pulled down over his eyes to keep out the intense blaze of light. You see his island, too, as clearly as though you were actually there, a shadowy witness of everything that takes place. You see him getting up of a morning, peevish and grouchy after a night of fever, of fitful sleeping and tossing and turning and semidelirious thinking about the future. You see his house and the one he had built for Topsy, where she spent her time "making the most impossible botches and bungles" in the way of clothes for the baby soon to be born. Having had his coffee he goes out to oversee his native labor. He had a large gang to supervise, sometimes one hundred or more. He holds his "sick parade," for there was always plenty of illness. The most common diseases were fever, diarrhea, and abscesses, and, of course, skin diseases innumerable. The men line up and he goes along the ranks making inquiries.

Asterisk. You sick long what?

No. 1. Me pever, Master (The *infirmier*, a "civilized" boy from Nouméa, takes the man's temperature while A. moves on.)

A. You sick long what?

No. 2. Belly b'long me, me hear 'im, 'e no good. Me tink belly b'long me, 'e run out, finish.

A. You been kaikai what name?

No. 2. No. Me kaikai rice, no more.

A. You no been kaikai crab?

No. 2. Yes, me bin kaikai one crab. (Probably at least twenty scavenger crabs.)

A (to *infirmier*). Toi, donne du sel d'Epsom à ce boy.

A. You sick long what?

No. 3. Arm b'long me 'e swell up. Me 'ear 'im, 'e strong. [Strong = hard and hot.]

A. All right. You go long house. By and by me put him on medicine. Tomorrow night after tomorrow, him not very good, me cut him arm belong you.

No. 3. All right, Master. Me tink very good you cut 'im.

There were always abscesses to cut, but the natives were stoical and had no fear of the knife. If he didn't cut them they would do it for themselves, which usually resulted in infection, so he had to put a taboo on self-cutting.

Sick parade over, the people are sent to work. Asterisk follows. It wasn't such an irksome job, the overseeing business, except for the deadly monotony. He sits on a log in a patch of shade, smokes his pipe and thinks. One gathers that there were times when he considered the necessity for thought a calamity which civilized human beings had brought upon themselves by too much education. If only one could vegetate, the mind a blank, how much more endurable life would be! Now and then he sings out, "Go ahead, there!" just to show them that he is not asleep. Occasionally he strolls around and pretends to be in a rage, merely to retain the proper respect due to an overseer. He returns to his little patch of shade, and a feeling of nostalgia for England comes over him. To hell with the South Seas! It was only the sentimental trippers viewing the islands from the deck of a comfortable steamer who raved about them. Let them try living on one for a year, for three months, for only three weeks. Lord! It would be good to be at home again! But what would he do in England? No, it was useless trying to delude himself. He had found it bad enough before the war. It would be a thousand times worse now with everybody being patriotic. All those young men in Kitchener's millions — are they really noble-minded, or merely sheep? If one of them had a grain of common sense would he be so noble? What a side-splitting farce war is, looked at dispassionately. Even here he felt occasional waves of hatred against the Germans surging through his silly self. Fortunately he had the time and the requisite detachment to think of the Germans he had known, just as harmless and as silly as himself, and so the rage quickly passed.

He thinks of Montevideo. It would be pleasant to go back there — to drop into the Club Uruguay at *apéritif* time, with the air thick with the fumes of Brazilian tobacco and absinthe and some *joven distinguido* with a shocking accent reciting Verlaine. Yes, it would be amusing, but only for a very short while. He would be heartily sick of the place before a week had passed.

Asterisk, Jr., who is on the way? Oh, Lord! Well, one thing was certain: it would never do to let himself get fond of the little brat. If he were to give way now, it would mean the renunciation of all that he really loved. Supposing he were to settle down in the islands for good, and try to make something of his son, for it was sure to be a boy. Plenty of white men had lived contentedly for years with Aoba women and had brought up half-caste children. But to begin with, these men were invariably the mental and physical inferiors of their native wives, and to end with, the half-castes were unspeakable. No, it wouldn't do at all, for a thousand reasons. The mockeries of civilization are one thing, but there is a world of difference between hating them and hurting one's head against them. As for "going native," that was impossible, for him, at any rate. We simply can't help being respectable Puritans. It isn't our fault. A fat duck who should set back the Mendelian clock a few hundred years and proclaim himself a wild bird of soaring flight would be justly laughed at by the rest of the poultry yard. No, the family is the product of thousands of years of evolution, and those who try to upset it, or to establish weird families of mixed breed on a cannibal island, only hurt themselves and make themselves ridiculous. There were no two ways about it — he would have to shift, leave Topsy and the baby when it came, clear out of these accursed

malarial islands for good. But the curious thing to reflect upon
was this: when he had gone, ten to one he would look back
over these years with pleasure. All the idyllic aspects of the
life would become grossly exaggerated in his eyes. Once away,
glamour would be sure to raise its deceiving and malicious
head. He might even be homesick for this Hell's Kitchen!
Wasn't that always the way of it? "There's no times like the
old times." "Ah, you should have sailed in my last ship, mates!
She was something like!" What complete unteachable asses
all men were!

These and innumerable other reflections scratched around
inside his bald middle-aged head as he went about his week-
day employments, and on Sunday one sees him sitting at his
table, scratching them down on paper in letters to his friend.
And so he went on down the road with Topsy until they came
to their first important milestone, the birth of Asterisk, Jr.,
whom he called Bilbil.

Then followed a really awful period for Asterisk. He was
torn by doubts as to what he should do. One day he would decide, definitely, finally, and irrevocably that he must leave
the islands at once. The next day he would reverse his decision just as irrevocably, and elaborate plans he had made
for Bilbil's upbringing. What a chance he now had to educate
a boy, and his own at that, according to his own ideas!

I am a crank. I know it. I have now got in my hand
most of the elements for an unordinary life — a little
savage mate, a fat baby, the island life where I can't
starve or want, a cynical pleasure in flaunting before all
the respectable Kerlonials tastes and fancies which I hope
to transmit to my heir, an opportunity for determining
that at least one child shall not grow up in damnable

ignorance of nature, shall not from babyhood be loaded
with the barnacles of convention. All that interests me
enormously. A return to Philistia does not. I have got a
unique chance now. If I were to throw it away I should
deserve whatever might befall me.

But it was not only the unique opportunity which made
him hesitate about leaving the islands. Little Bilbil had a
great deal to do with it. The flow of affection toward him
grew stronger from week to week. It greatly worried the
father to find how deeply the current ran. Then he would
see the grown-up, half-caste son of some planter or trader,
arrogant, shiftless, good for nothing, and he would say to himself, "There goes my Bilbil twenty years from now," and he
would rush back to his little "iron hell" to add a postscript
to a letter in which he had outlined ambitious plans for his
son's education:

> The sooner I get rid of him the better. . . . I have
> been fighting hard to convince myself that I have no color
> prejudices, but I chuck up now. . . . I am so afraid that
> if I take Bilbil away and get him among whiter things,
> I shall straightway begin to hate him. I know I should.
> No, I have made a horrid mistake. The only real way out
> is to end the whole business before it goes any further.

Whereupon he would again complete arrangements with
some decent colonial of his acquaintance who would agree to
take charge of Topsy and Bilbil and see to it that they would
have a comfortable and contented life after his departure.
And again these plans would be unmade, and so it went on,
week after week, month after month. In one of his letters
he says, "I don't suppose you have passed so many sleepless

nights in your life as I have during the past year," and no doubt he was right in supposing this.

One day Topsy came in for a talk, and she told him another baby was on the way. It was the last straw for Asterisk. He seizes his head in his hands and sits thus for a long time. Then he takes his pen, worn to a mere stub by this time, no doubt, with recounting on paper plans and canceled plans and all the cares of family life, and wearily passes on the news to his friend, adding:

> It is abominable. Topsy will have to go back to Aoba to have that child *au naturel* and leave Bilbil with me. One small *métis* may be *mets délicieux,* but two would be a surfeit, an orgy, an impossibility, an Oxford breakfast.

There was something comical about all this as there is in many a tragic situation. Well, what was to be done now?

I may have given the impression that Asterisk's time and thought were wholly occupied with his personal and family cares, but this was not the case. Despite frequent attacks of illness, the intense heat, and the dreary routine of plantation life, his mind was perpetually active. I can't find that he deteriorated to any extent, intellectually, for all his seven and a half years of solitude. In fact, his mind during the last two years seems to have been keener and healthier than at first. He was a careful observer and sent his friend many a lively account of island happenings, many a vivid picture of something he had seen on the plantation or in the bush.

In February 1919, the second baby was born — dead. On this occasion Topsy had nearly a week of agony and was herself at the point of death when the child was delivered. At that moment she gave Asterisk a sudden brief glimpse into her strange little soul.

> She was quite certain that she was going to die, but seemed equally convinced that I was going with her wherever she went. "By and by two feller 'e go where? By an by two feller 'e go same place? 'E where? 'E long England? 'E long Nouméa? Me tink 'e stop long way too much. By and by two feller 'e go longa steamer?
>
> "Bald 'ead, you sabby koumala [sweet potato] w'en me cook 'im long you, me burn 'im? By God, me sorry too much long that!"

I had quite forgotten the incident. She had done even as Alfred the Great on one occasion, and I had cursed her heartily. She had evidently been consumed with shame for the heinous offense and seized the nearness of death as an opportunity for unburdening herself. Today she is merry as a cricket again, and if I were out of sight would be up and off to her beloved sea for a swim.

I could write indefinitely about these letters, for they are of absorbing interest to me; but I hope I have said enough and quoted enough to persuade some of those who have not read the book to turn to it for themselves, if it is still procurable. It was published in America in 1923, by Small, Maynard & Company. It rarely happens that a man of Asterisk's background and education has had the courage — or perhaps I should say foolhardiness — to do what he did, and of the few who have done so, not one, in so far as I know, has left a record of the experiment to be compared with his.

At last, in November 1919, he left the New Hebrides, after having arranged for Bilbil to be adopted into a planter's family. Topsy was to remain with this family until the spirit should move her to return to her beloved Aoba. Asterisk went to Australia, and with returning health, all his zest for life and for new experience came back to him. He was again full of plans, but some of his illusions and his longing for the romantic life seem to have been knocked out of him, temporarily at least. He was going to Norfolk Island to make his fortune extracting oil of lemon. He was going to England to seek employment in a bookshop, and he asks his friend to make inquiries about possible openings in this field against his return. He was going back to schoolmastering and was considering an offer in Sydney; and he was considering another offer as a commercial traveler. But the longing for romance and freedom seems to have been dormant merely, not dead. Some months later, on an island in French Polynesia, where he found employment as secretary to a phosphate company, he was again convinced that he had found the kind of life he had so long hoped for. The last paragraph in his last letter to his English friend reads:

Just at present the moon is between the quarter and the full, giving light enough to read by, and the palms and the surf would make me cry if they didn't make me so gorgeously happy. I think I am just beginning to know what happiness beauty can give.

Not two years after this letter was written, my own trail in the Pacific chanced to cross that of Asterisk, on the island of Tahiti. He had left the phosphate island and his secretarial position there and had come to Tahiti apparently to make his home there, but after a brief sojourn on that most beautiful of islands he had moved on again into the blue — no one knew where. At that time his letters to his English friend had just been published under the title *Isles of Illusion,* and it had been my good fortune to find a copy in Papeete. As I have said, I read the letters with deep interest and made inquiries about Asterisk in the town. One man said: "Do you mean that insufferable Englishman who talked like a book?" Another said, "He's gone, and a good riddance, too." A third spoke of him as "the most interesting fellow I've met in years, and the most unhappy." But his impressions, he said, were only impressions. His meetings with Asterisk had been few, usually at the Restaurant du Port on the monthly steamer day. He told me where Asterisk had lived, in one of the country districts, thirty-five miles from Papeete. I decided to go there and see the place for myself.

Twenty-five years ago Tahiti's round-the-island road was little better than a cart track, rough going for bicycles, but one could manage it. A light film of cloud had settled around the shoulders of the mountains far in the interior, but their jagged peaks jutted through into the clear sky above, and the lowlands along the coast were in full sunshine. Far inland, against the blue battlemented cliffs I could see at times flocks of snow-white terns gleaming and vanishing in sunlight and shadow like bits of silver paper, and the waterfalls tumbling over the headwalls of valleys were so remote that they seemed to be hanging motionless. Not a sound, of bird or beast or man, broke the afternoon stillness. I heard only the faint roar of the surf along the barrier reefs, and that is not sound but a part of Silence itself to one who has lived long on tropical islands.

The house where Asterisk had lived was far from the road. I followed a footpath pointed out to me by a native of the district. This led through a stretch of low, partly swampy ground pitted with the holes of land crabs and densely shaded by great *mapé* trees with their buttressed trunks and looped and twisted roots that seem to writhe and turn as you gaze at them. I waded a river and soon came to rising ground. Another five minutes brought me within view of the sea, and there on a point of land jutting into the lagoon I found Asterisk's dwelling.

It was just what it should have been for that spot, built in the native style, with walls of plaited bamboo, a roof of thatch steeply pitched, and low overhanging eaves furnishing a pleasant veranda all around, and floored with coral sand. It requires but little time for an abandoned dwelling to deteriorate in the tropics, and Asterisk's was in a forlorn condition. It contained but one room whose windows had been screened with gauze mosquito netting, but this was rotting away, strips of it hanging down, swaying to and fro in the breeze. The thatch roof also was decaying and there were many places where the rain had soaked through. The lawn was now growing tall and rank, weeds and bushes springing up everywhere.

Whatever furniture the house had contained was sold or given away, I suppose, when Asterisk left; but from a nail driven into one of the posts supporting the roof hung a discarded linen coat and an old pandanus-leaf hat, and in a corner was a walking stick that had been cut from the bush. They were Asterisk's, undoubtedly. Men speak of "the souls of things." They have them, or, rather, they take on aspects of the souls of their owners. There was something bizarre, outlandish about the coat and hat, and something primly "schoolmasterish" in the way they hung from the nail that told me whose they had been. And the walking stick as well: there were green stains upon it as though it had been used for lashing furiously at twigs and bushes and the heads of grasses.

I walked a long way down the beach — there was no one either white or native living in that vicinity — and came slowly back to the house. Viewed in the light of late afternoon it looked very forlorn and desolate, so I turned my back on it and looked out to sea. I had my copy of Asterisk's letters with me, and choosing a shady spot I sat down to glance through them again, and immediately I had a sense of the nearness of his eager, hopeful, restless, dissatisfied spirit.

I have not yet stopped shuddering at Sydney. I fear very much that London would displease me also. I look at the illustrated papers and see the pictures of the smug crowds. . . .

I could be very happy in Devonshire, perhaps, as long as it didn't rain, but, unfortunately, I couldn't spend the rest of my life in Devonshire in summertime. . . .

Oh, England is a beastly place. Just think of the rules, the chains, and fetters of brass. . . . Do you think there is one person in London who could like or even tolerate a really free man and an unconventional life? And then, when one thinks of the country — *sacré nom d'un nom d'un nom!* . . .

At present I simply long to be in London. I am fast coming to the conclusion that fireside travel is much pleasanter than the reality. There are fewer disillusionments and one can pick one's company. . . .

I should love to go into a "retreat" for two whole years, to wipe myself clean, to try and get my mind free from my beastly body. If only such places existed without the interference of some non-sensical creed I would go. I want to live. I want neither to be praised nor blamed. . . .

I was thinking the other day of my curiously futile life, and the phrase flashed across my malaria-befuddled mind, "The aspirations of the irresolute in common with the aspirates of the illiterate are often dropped, often misplaced, always misunderstood." This is a fair sample of my mental condition. I am forgetting how to talk, how to think, even how to eat. . . .

I am irresistibly drawn eastward sometimes . . . I am sure that it is only amongst the very old things of the world that one can find that blessed state where things are not classified as good and evil, "done" or "not done." . . .

I think that the ideal South Sea island must be left as a beautiful dream. . . . I feel sad about it, but an unsatisfied longing is better than a shattered dream. . . .

For a few pounds or even for nothing as a supercargo on a schooner, I can reach in a few days realms of bliss. And with the saved money I can live as I want to live, and know for myself what I am convinced is there awaiting me. . . .

Thus it was always with Asterisk — forever hopeful after repeated disillusionments, thinking that the place where he was not was the place where "further beauty and fuller peace" awaited him. As I turned the pages I came upon one letter in which he had sent his friend copies of two poems he loved: rondeaus of Charles d'Orléans written in the fifteenth century. They are both exquisite things, but this one chimed in best with my mood of the moment, with the drowsy spirit of the afternoon, and my thoughts of Asterisk:

A HAPPY HEDONIST

Laissez-moy penser à mon aise,
Hélas! donnez m'en le loysir.
Je devise avecques Plaisir
Combien que ma bouche se taise.

Quand Merencolie mauvaise
Me vient maintes fois assaillir,
Laissez-moy penser à mon aise,
Hélas! donnez m'en le loysir.

Car afin que mon cueur rapaise,
J'appelle Plaisant-Souvenir,
Qui tantost me vient resfouïr.
Pour ce, Pour Dieu! ne vous deplaise
Laissez-moy penser à mon aise.

The refrain seemed to ring pensively in the air, to die away slowly, and to dissolve at last in the golden peace of the afternoon. I remained seated for a long while, watching the changing colors on the lagoon, thinking of Asterisk, wondering why he had left such a lovely spot, where he had gone, and what shape his dream would now take to lure him on.

This was twenty-five years ago. Asterisk may be dead by now. If not, he must be close to seventy. Perhaps he is still following the quest. But on what farthest star, I wonder, is the true home of the searcher for beauty, happiness, and the free life?

V. Rivnac

W<small>E BEGAN</small> to meet in spirit, so to speak, twenty years before either of us was aware of the other's existence. Friend-
ships are, sometimes, prepared for long in advance of the day
when the friends-to-be meet in the flesh. So it was in this case.
Antonin Dvořák, the great Czech composer — or rather his
living spirit expressed in his music — was the means of bringing Milos Rivnac and me together, but Chance had arranged
the place and time of meeting: the island of Tahiti, in the year
1927. Comparing notes on that occasion we discovered that
we had both heard Dvořák's *New World Symphony* for the
first time in the year 1907: he in his homeland, then a part
of the Austro-Hungarian Empire, and I as a freshman at Grinnell College, in my home state, Iowa.

I was then in my late teens, and as ignorant of music in the
high sense as most young men of that epoch, born and raised
in small towns of the prairie country. On that particular midwinter afternoon I was crossing the campus on my way to the
college library to make an attempt to prepare in half an hour
for an Ethics quiz which was to come at one-fifteen. Passing
the chapel I heard strains of pipe-organ music and stepped inside for a moment to listen. The chapel was empty save for
Professor Scheve at the organ. In less than two minutes I was

rapt away from any further thought of Ethics, and when I next became conscious of the present moment, Professor Scheve was leaving the chapel by the side door below the choir stalls. He was unaware of his audience of one, sitting in the back row of seats, and little could he have guessed the effect the music was to have upon his solitary listener. It was then well past the hour for the examination, but I felt not even a twinge of remorse for having missed it.

What I had just heard was Dvořák's *New World Symphony,* arranged for pipe organ, from midway in the first movement on to the end. As I listened doors swung apart, revealing what was, indeed, a new world to me. I left the chapel and walked north beyond the town, along a country road where the stubble fields, lightly powdered with snow, were of the palest gold in the wan sunshine of that February afternoon. Perhaps I took a northerly direction because the first part of the second movement seemed to require it. Music that appeals to me deeply is often associated with landscape, but idealized, spiritualized: of the Earth and *not* of it at the same time. The Largo of *The New World Symphony,* whenever or wherever heard from that day to this, calls up the melancholy beauty of the prairie country as seen in late afternoon sunlight of a windless, midwinter day.

I am twenty years distant from my first meeting with Rivnac and it is a temptation to proceed in leisurely fashion, describing many happy and memorable events by the way; but in that case I would be compelled to write a volume rather than a sketch. The reader knows of the dark events the world shared in common during a fateful four of the years: 1914–1918; and no Czech reader needs to be reminded of the happiness, so woefully brief, brought to his own countrymen when their ancient homeland was theirs at last, to be enjoyed in freedom.

On the island of Tahiti was a little hotel called Chez Rivnac which had been recently opened, but I did not know that the proprietor was a Czech until one afternoon while making a bicycle journey around the island, I turned off the main road into the grassy lane leading to the hotel.

Of all tropical islands that I have seen, Tahiti comes nearest to being the earthly counterpart of Tennyson's Land of the Lotos-Eaters. All the flowers growing there are lotus blooms in the mythical sense, particularly the hibiscus which, in its varied forms and colors, is, surely, the loveliest of all scentless flowers that grow in tropical or subtropical climates. And it is always in blossom, although individual blossoms have so brief a life: one day, two at the longest. Lines from "The Lotos-Eaters" and "The Choric Song" were running through my head as I followed the lane toward Rivnac's place:

> All day the wind breathes low with mellower tone;
> Through every hollow cave and alley lone
> Round and round the spicy downs the yellow Lotos-dust
>   is blown . . .

> In the afternoon they came unto a land
> In which it seemèd always afternoon . . .

So it seems on Tahiti. It was midafternoon as I approached the hotel which stands at the border of a lagoon as calm, often, as a mountain lake, perfectly reflecting heaped-up masses of pure white cloud drifting slowly above it.

In the profound sunny stillness I heard phonograph music of a kind I least expected to hear. As I halted to listen, leaning against my bicycle, Tahiti vanished, and in the imagination I was again walking north along a country road in Iowa, where the stubble fields, lightly powdered with snow, were of the palest gold in the wan sunshine of a February afternoon. A moment later I entered the lounge, Chez Rivnac.

It was a spacious, airy room with a balustrade on the western side separating it from a terrace floored with white sand. A row of *burau* trees, with broad leaves like those of our American linden, protected the terrace and the lounge itself from the afternoon sunlight, so that the room was filled with a cool, greenish, sunlight-dappled shade.

The only occupant was a man of huge proportions stretched out in an easy chair near an old, hand-winding, cabinet-size phonograph. His eyes were closed as he listened with an air of absorbed attention to the second movement of Dvořák's *New World Symphony*. He did not hear me enter so I stood at a little distance until the record came to an end. As he opened his eyes an expression of mingled surprise and annoyance passed over his broad smooth face. With an effort he heaved himself up from the chair and regarded me for a moment in silence. Then he said: *"Vous desirez . . . ?"*

"Please continue with the symphony," I replied. "I'd like to listen."

The stiffness in his manner vanished. *"Bon!"* he said, in a relieved voice. Slowly he lowered himself into the easy chair which, despite its sturdiness, complained in every joint and tenon as it received his weight again.

"Henriette!" he called, at the same time waving me to a chair.

A native girl around thirty, bare-legged and barefooted, with a *pareu* fastened beneath her arms and reaching to her knees, appeared at an inner doorway. She was fat and homely, with a most engaging smile, indicating boundless friendliness and good will. As she stood in the doorway, a slender shaft of sunlight piercing the leaves of one of the *burau* trees fell upon her face. The shaft of sunshine made the smile more golden still as the light was reflected from two gold teeth.

"*Haere noa*" (Continue), said Rivnac, with a gesture toward the phonograph. She was his record changer, for he could not have listened with much enjoyment had he been compelled to struggle up from his chair at the end of each record and do the changing himself. She brought each disk to him before placing it on the phonograph to be sure that she played them in the right order; then seated herself cross-legged on the floor, falling into a kind of waking trance while the music was playing. *The New World Symphony* was not Henriette's idea of music. It was *popaa* — foreign music, the kind that white men, or some of them, so strangely enjoy. Rivnac had to bounce her awake at the end of each record with a bellowed "Henriette!" The trancelike expression would then change to the golden smile as she rose to her feet.

When the symphony came to an end I ordered two bottles of ice-cold beer. Henriette — who was everything, Chez Rivnac, from barmaid and headwaitress to leader of the dancers when a gay evening was in full swing — brought the beer and placed it on a little table between us. It was excellent Dutch beer — Amstel; and for some time we enjoyed it in silence as we had the music. Presently we began to talk, and it was then that we learned that both of us had heard *The New World Symphony* for the first time in 1907.

"And now you come to my place these many years later,"

said Rivnac, "and we hear it for the first time together. *C'est drôle . . . fantastique, plutôt.*"

He was at home in 1907, he said, and then corrected himself. "At home, but *not* at home. My country was then a part of Austria-Hungary. But now . . . it is Czechoslovakia." He pronounced the name with an air of reverence; with an intonation that indicated deep content, wonder and incredulity, as though the glorious change could not be true and he expected to wake up, presently, and learn that Czechoslovakia had only a dream reality. He then asked where I had been in 1907. I told him that I was an American, from Iowa in the Middle West, and had heard the symphony in the chapel at Grinnell College.

"I-o-wah . . . I-o-wah," he repeated, musingly. "I do not know that place."

"You have heard, surely, of Spillville, a little town in northeastern Iowa?" I replied.

He shook his head. "Why should I have heard of it?"

"Dvořák lived there in the early nineties, while writing *The New World Symphony.*"

He stared at me. "Impossible," he said. I told him that, for a Czech and a lover of Dvořák's music, he was surprisingly ignorant of the events in the life of his great countryman. He did not, in fact, know that Dvořák had spent the years 1892–1895 in the U.S.A.; that *The New World Symphony* was completed in 1893; or that — as I am convinced — the inspiration for it came, in part, from Iowa and the country thereabout, as he had seen it from the vantage point of Spillville.

Rivnac could not believe what I had told him, but later when he had verified the matter for himself he became keenly interested in Spillville and wanted to know all about the place.

I told him that I made only an occasional pilgrimage there, but described the little town, predominantly Czech in population, set in the midst of some of the most beautiful pastoral country in the Middle West. His interest increased on learning that the town was Czech. Did the people honor Dvořák while he was there? Had they honored him since? Did I see the house where he had lived? I described the house, a modest two-story brick dwelling not far from the church; but I was reluctant to tell him that a sign over the door read: "Antonin Dvořák lived in this house when he wrote the *Humoresque*." For, although it is said that *The New World Symphony* was, for the most part, written in the East before he went to Iowa, I am convinced by the spirit of the music itself that it must have been revised if not completely rewritten during his sojourn at Spillville.

Our love for Dvořák's music, *The New World Symphony* in particular, made a kind of secret bond between us, and the result was that I saw a side of Rivnac's nature that not many were aware of. A considerable number of his acquaintances thought of him only as a hotel man who had the gift, with small means, of making his guests comfortable and content. His deepest feelings were never on display, least of all his feelings with respect to his homeland. Many people did not know that he was Czech; to them he was, merely, a cosmopolitan from somewhere in Europe who spoke several languages well and who had a smattering of others. Tahiti has never been an island overrun with tourists. It is too remote, and the means of travel are far from adequate from the tourist point of view. Rivnac rarely had as many as a score of guests at one time, often no more than half a dozen, and sometimes none at all.

I recall evenings when the guests were mostly local people: whites, natives, half-castes, no-castes, with a sprinkling of others from the outside world; when the food, the music, the dancing and the fun were thoroughly Tahitian in character. Henriette was in her element on such occasions and a great contributor to the gaiety of the evening. When the guitars, ukuleles, accordions and drums struck into a fast Tahitian hula, with a whoop of joy she would join the other dancers, competing successfully with slim young girls scarcely half her age.

One evening a young American, recently arrived, was among the guests. He had come to Tahiti "to live, really live," as he put it to me. He was rather vague as to what he meant by this, but judging by what he did, I gathered that his idea of really living was to sit under a breadfruit tree with a beautiful, scantily clad Tahitian girl at his feet, gazing rapturously into his eyes while she sang island songs to a guitar accompaniment. He had found the girl and was, apparently, in heaven; or, it would have been heaven except for the fact that he spoke neither Tahitian nor French, and her knowledge of English was confined to a few expressions such as "Hello! Give me cigarette," and the like. They conversed by glances, and his were so adoring that he failed to notice what was clear to an observer, that hers revealed more than a hint of boredom. She was a pretty little thing, and a superb dancer in the island fashion. He was deeply smitten, and it annoyed his companion that a man who could only gaze at her yet wanted, and expected, to receive her undivided attention.

Later on this evening the young man, who had had too many rum punches, was in a rather maudlin condition. His girl had left him, and this was a serious blow to his self-esteem —

he had a good deal of that. He sat alone at his table staring gloomily at her. She was having a gay time dancing with native companions and appeared to have forgotten his existence.

There came a break in the festivities; the musicians and native dancers were having a well-earned rest. People sat at their tables sipping drinks, and a buzz of conversation filled the air. The young man continued to stare moodily at his girl, but a little later he rose unsteadily and made his way to the piano at the far end of the lounge. He sat down before it and started to play, in an effort, it seemed, to attract attention to himself; but no one paid the least attention to him. Presently he began to sing, in an excellent but lugubrious voice. The song was "Going Home."

It may be remembered that the words of this song are set to the air in the Largo movement in *The New World Symphony*. Still no one listened; so I thought at first — then I saw Rivnac standing at the doorway leading to the terrace. Hands on hips he stared at the back of the piano player, an expression of shocked amazement and unbelief on his face. As he told me, later, he had never before heard this song and listened only long enough to be certain of the air. He then strode to the piano, seized the young man under the arms and lifted him from the stool as though he had been a child. Setting him on his feet facing him he held him at arm's length, his eyes blazing with anger. The young man stared back in a puzzled, maudlin fashion. I did not hear what he said, but Rivnac's only reply was to seize him by the collar and propel him, protestingly, out of the lounge and across the lawn to the little guest house where he was lodged; or he may have tossed him into the lagoon. At any rate, that was my last view of the singer of "Going Home," who did go home, I believe, by the next north-bound steamer.

There are, I know, people who think that the music of the Largo movement appeals to shallow emotions, and I have both heard and read estimates of the symphony as a whole that are far from being my own. They have never seemed to me high enough, and so often they are in terms of music critics, mindful of their reputations, afraid, seemingly, of showing enthusiasm lest it betray them to the smiles of other critics.

My bump of veneration for music critics and interpreters was, formerly, high, but the older I grow the more convinced I become that we laymen, ignorant of music in the technical sense, probably know as much about its meaning, in human terms, as many of the critics. It is well to remember what Frank Moore Colby said of them: "Music critics in many cases probably do not hear the music at all. They are deafened by the noise of their own expository intentions." It seems to me that the great composers, although they may know what they wish to say in terms of their own inner experience, cannot and do not announce, dogmatically, what their music shall mean to *us*. Only the critics do that. And often their comments are mere displays of erudition concerning the form of a particular work, as though form were the only important thing to be considered.

Whether justifiably or not, I have come to accept my own estimate of *The New World Symphony* as final, and valid — for me. I have lived with it too long to do otherwise. It seems to me the most inspiring of unfulfilled prophecies, and, at the same time, by implication, the most heartbreaking commentary in advance, on the history thus far of the twentieth century that has been, or could be, recorded in music. I cannot believe that the time will ever come when it will seem dated, old; for it is a prophecy, not only of what might have been, and yet may be, but also a somber reminder of what has been. It is a moving commentary on Man's alternate hopes and despairs in the long unending struggle for a better world; and the noblest themes in it speak of the renewal of courage and faith at the darkest moments when he has nothing but faith to cling to.

It may be well to add that my "expository intentions" are toward myself alone. I am not saying that Dvořák would, or that anyone else should, agree with this interpretation.

But Rivnac did, with enough variance of opinion to give us matter for discussion when there were few or no guests to occupy his time and attention. We were in agreement about the second movement. To us it was sacred for reasons we did not attempt to define. Rivnac would snort with indignation when he remembered "Going Home," but smile somewhat ruefully, thinking of the young man whom he had hustled so brusquely out of the lounge on the night when he sang the song. But who wrote those words, he wanted to know. What small-souled wretch had dared to cheapen and vulgarize such music; to attempt enclosing it within the framework of his own mean understanding?

We discussed other matters, of course, besides Dvořák's music. Rivnac had a keen sense of humor, and human nature of the globe-trotting kind as it sometimes displayed itself Chez Rivnac gave him matter for comment as amusing as it was instructive. But he was silent when he "discussed" his food. I sometimes dropped in for lunch or dinner when there were no guests, and sat at an adjoining table. He had a

Gargantuan appetite. One would have said that food had been prepared for twenty people, and since no one had come to eat it except myself, he was determined to see that none of it should go to waste. The main reason why he was usually on the verge of bankruptcy was the abundance of food prepared for hypothetical guests. If they failed to appear, trust a Tahitian hotel staff and a landlord with the appetite of a dozen harvest hands to consume the food prepared. There was nothing Henriette enjoyed more than to see someone eat, with gusto, an enormous meal. Her smile was golden indeed as she cleared away Rivnac's empty plates. *"Aué!"* she would say. *"Paia 'huru paia!"* (He's full up to the neck!)

Rivnac's dream, if ever he could afford to make the journey, was to return to Czechoslovakia; to see his homeland in being, free from the shackles that had bound it to the Austro-Hungarian Empire. One day while speaking of this he said, "If only Dvořák could have lived to see it so!" I said that, in my opinion, Dvořák had a wider conception of the future; that the New World he dreamed of was not one made of small lands however homogeneous in character, but a New World in very truth: all such homelands bound together in harmony by the logic of changed world conditions which made this so necessary if only men could be brought to see it, and to accept, freely and willingly, a common destiny.

"But of course," said Rivnac. "None but fools could doubt it. Why did the U.S.A. under your great President Wilson wish to see Czechoslovakia separated from the Austro-Hungarian Empire? Wilson knew, as Dvořák knew, that we Czechs are like you Americans: lovers of freedom and believers in the rights and the dignity of men as individuals. There was no hope of a New World Symphony under the Hapsburgs. But there was, and is, with Czechoslovakia as a nucleus, a rallying point for all freedom lovers in Central Europe. One day if we survive as a nation, the New World of a united Europe will begin to have reality. . . . Henriette!"

In she came, with the golden smile that was like a confirmation of Rivnac's belief in the future, indicating good will of world-wide proportions. He wanted to play some passages from the E minor Symphony which, he felt, confirmed his belief that Dvořák had Czechoslovakia in mind as one of the foundation stones of the new world of his dreams. No matter how far we might stray in conversation, we were like a pair of homing birds, one of which weighed nearly three hundred pounds, returning to dreams of Tomorrow, already prophesied, in music, by the great Czech composer.

During the nineteen-twenties and early thirties I did not own a radio. In so far as world events were concerned I was, perhaps, something of a human ostrich, but with my head in the clouds, not buried in the sand. I remember writing a sonnet in reply to a friend who had reproached me for what he thought was my ignorance of and indifference to contemporary history-in-the-making in Europe and elsewhere, and my love for history-without-history — the best kind, in my opinion — exemplified by life on Tahiti. The concluding lines of the sonnet expressed my feeling at the time:

> Atlas has mighty limbs; my strength is small;
> And when I offered aid, "My child," he said,
> "I have more helpers than I want, or need.
> The world is served in many ways. If all
> Stand here with me, and sweat, and groan, and bleed,
> Who shall see the glory overhead?"

It was this glory, not only above and around but ahead of us, to which I gave absorbed attention. I saw it growing and brightening. Since I spent much time listening to Silence in preference to radio programs, the beauty of Silence was enhanced because I could hear through it, as though coming from beyond it, themes from *The New World Symphony*. As I am of a sanguine temperament, a firm believer in the fundamental decency of human beings in general, and with a deep faith in mankind's inherited, collective wisdom, the possibility of another World War, to say nothing of a third one in our own lifetimes, was, to me, not even a remote possibility. It was not conceivable.

Then, in 1935, after fifteen years of living according to my own desires, most of the time spent on small islands in the Pacific, I felt for the first time, unmistakably, a premonition of horror which, until then, I could not even imagine as possible in the twentieth century. Night — dreadful Night, was moving out from Germany, spreading over Central Europe, and gradually, imperceptibly darkening the light of day for all mankind. I wish there were some way of describing the effect of the premonition upon the human spirit on islands such as Tahiti, for example, having so little contact except by static-troubled air waves with the outside world. In my own case, I became conscious of what might be called invisible gloom deepening daily; and from the midst of it came the sound of a human voice, if it may be called human. It came, via radio, from a place called the Sports Palace, in Berlin. It was all but inconceivable that the voice and the message it conveyed were that of the accepted, recognized leader of Germany, the homeland of Goethe, Beethoven, Mozart, Schiller; the homeland of Professor Scheve, beloved by everyone at Grinnell, to whom I owe my first hearing of *The New World Symphony*. Never before, surely, has a voice from the depths had such power to persuade millions of persons that they, too, were of the depths, and to draw them there after him.

My hearing of the voice was another experience shared with Rivnac. As Night deepened over Europe he had bought a secondhand radio, the best he could afford. Late at night he was able to hear short-wave broadcasts from various European cities, Prague among them. After that there were no more merry evenings Chez Rivnac.

One moonlight night I was cycling homeward after a visit with friends who lived beyond his place on the west coast. It was after midnight when I came to the entrance to his lane. I turned off there, thinking he might still be up.

On a night of full moon, the little hotel with its individual guest houses of bamboo and thatch, the shadows of coconut palms moving gently back and forth over the smooth lawn, did not seem to belong to Earth. All was silent there, save for the breeze rustling the palm fronds and rocking the long-stemmed banana leaves that flashed like green mirrors in the moonlight. The door of Rivnac's room was open and a shaft of lamplight fell upon the turf outside. He sat before his radio, hunched down as closely to it as his huge belly would permit, his shadow blocking from view all other objects in the room.

How was it possible, I thought, that a voice, though it came from the depths of dreadful Night, could disturb the peace and beauty of such a night as this, on an island lost "in the moonlit solitudes mild of the midmost ocean"? No lotos-eater of two thousand years ago could have protested with deeper feeling than one on the island of Tahiti as he regarded the Pandora's Box only a few steps distant from where he stood:

> Let us alone. Time driveth onward fast,
> And in a little while our lips are dumb.
> Let us alone. What is it that will last?
> All things are taken from us, and become
> Portions and parcels of the dreadful Past.
> Let us alone. What pleasure can we have
> To war with Evil?

I need not remind the reader of the Evil growing to monstrous proportions during the years 1937–1938; and how the leaders of great nations, in so far as their actions were concerned, might have been kings among the lotos-eaters, saying:

> Let us alone. What need have we to war
> With Evil? Let us make a bold pretense
> That Evil is a friend. Open the door.
> Perhaps the best defense is no defense.
> Be brave, for passive courage is sublime,
> And we will bring you peace within our time . . .
> We think.

And when they *were* let alone to promise it, their passivity resulting in the betrayal of Czechoslovakia and Hitler's seizure of the country, even on Tahiti we heard the news of the latter event on the day after it happened.

I had avoided going to Rivnac's place during the Munich negotiations, for what comfort was there to offer him? Nevertheless, at the time when the Huns stormed into Prague, I found myself biking down the familiar lane, not knowing what I could do, or even hoped to do, upon reaching the end of it.

Henriette saw me approaching and came out to meet me. The smile was still faintly there, but a puzzled, worried one on this occasion. Henriette's world was Tahiti, the only one she knew or cared about. She had scarcely more knowledge of what was happening in Europe than the coconut palm against which I leaned my bicycle.

"He's here?" I asked.

She nodded. "But there's no use your going in. He won't speak. He won't say a word to anyone, not even me. He just sits there."

An attempt to explain in detail would have been futile; but Henriette had at least heard of Hitler. She knew that he was a *taata ino* — an evil man whom Rivnac hated. So I said, merely, that Hitler was making trouble in Rivnac's country. "Do you still have some of that good Dutch beer — Amstel?" I asked.

"Yes, but that's no use either. I brought him a bottle and he didn't even notice it. After a while I took it away. It was open so I drank the beer myself. No sense in wasting it." At my request she agreed to try again, later, when I called for it.

He was sitting in his stout chair near the phonograph, and I could see no outward change except that instead of his usual greeting he gave me a barely perceptible nod, and then appeared to have forgotten my existence. I sat in my customary chair and presently glanced toward the bar. Henriette was there, watching us. She brought the beer, glancing at Rivnac as she set it down and then at me, as though to say, "You see? It's useless," and going quietly out again.

To my relief, Rivnac presently noticed the glass I had filled for him and drained and set it down again, but without a glance at me. Silence was no embarrassment in his presence. We had many a talk, sometimes lighted with a warm glow of agreement, sometimes by sparks of conflicting opinion colliding with one another and flying off in all directions. And there were times when we sat without a word exchanged, each of us engaged in his own reflections.

Presently I took my courage in my hands, far from certain that what I was about to do would not prove to be the worst possible thing I could have done, under the circumstances. I went to the shelf of record albums and took from it the one we loved so much. It was falling to pieces and had to be handled carefully, for the Manila holders for each record were worn through at the bottoms. Without glancing at Rivnac I wound the machine, put in a fresh needle and set it gently down on the record beginning the fourth movement.

It was then night in Europe; night in a double sense in Czechoslovakia. The voice from the depths may have been blaring through loud-speakers at street corners in the beautiful old city of Prague and fouling the ether waves the world around; but we were not aware of it Chez Rivnac: at least I was not. It was as though I were hearing a new fourth movement; for music in the high sense is no shallow pool, revealing on the surface all that is contained beneath. It is a never-failing spring of living water, to quench thirst of many kinds; to give refreshment, solace, new powers of endurance under the cruelest blows of Fate; courage, hope, according to the infinite needs of the human spirit. I remembered what Rivnac had said and felt the truth of it. It seemed to me that Dvořák was speaking, now, for and to his homeland. And I heard the voice of Czechoslovakia Itself, the collective voice of its people as individuals, comforting and heartening one another, all of them united in spirit wherever they might be, and holding fast to faith in the future.

I was so deeply moved that, for a moment, I forgot Rivnac.

He sat forward as though about to rise, his hands grasping the arms of his chair, his head lowered like that of an old bull. When, at the end of the movement he looked at me, the light burning in his eyes told me that we had shared another first experience, one never to be forgotten.

World War II was in progress when, later, I went down the lane to his place. I had just returned from the U.S.A. where I remained longer than I had expected to. Tahiti's contact with the outside world had vanished save for one small cargo steamer which called at the island at four-month intervals on its way to Australia. I had not heard from Rivnac, nor had I thought of him often, for the somber events of 1940–1941, when England was fighting alone, engaged all men's numbed attention. But in San Francisco, a few days before I was to board ship for my return to Tahiti, I went to the Sherman & Clay music store and bought a superb recording of *The New World Symphony* by the Philadelphia Symphony Orchestra under the direction of Leopold Stokowski. I could think of no gift which Rivnac would appreciate more. The records in his old album were all but worn-out, and there were places where the needle remained in the same groove and "Henriette!" would be stirred from her waking trance before she was well into it.

Not a light was shown on the little cargo steamer nor did we sight another ship throughout the course of the voyage. Early on the morning of the fifteenth day Tahiti and her neighboring island, Moorea, rose from the sea in all their lonely beauty, and in my joy at seeing them once more I forgot what was happening elsewhere in the world. I thought only of the happy day just beginning, and of the moment so near at hand when I would walk down the steamer's gangplank. But I had not been five minutes ashore when I learned that Rivnac was dead.

The death of an old friend, wherever one may live, leaves a great gap in the lives of those who survive him, and this is more than ever the case in a small island world such as Tahiti. One is reminded of it constantly. Whichever way you look, there is the empty space where your friend had been. As I got down from the bus at Rivnac's gate it was hard to believe that I would not find him at the other end of the lane. The fact that I had the new recording of the E minor Symphony in a parcel under my arm contributed to the illusion that he would be sitting in the familiar chair near the phonograph.

One enters the hotel through an anteroom at the southeast corner, three steps down from the lounge. It is floored with coral sand and being sheltered from the afternoon sunlight it is a cool and pleasant place for loafing as the sun slopes westward. On the inner wall hangs a portrait of Rivnac, painted by a Russian artist, and meant to be a friendly caricature. I call it a portrait because it is Rivnac himself: the huge flesh-and-blood Rivnac known to all his guests. As I paused to look at it again, after many months of absence, the only emotion I felt was a kind of numbed unbelief. He couldn't be dead. He was there, surely, in the lounge. I mounted the steps leading to it and looked in.

The room was empty save for Henriette, who was belatedly sweeping the floor. Her back was toward me, and the sunlight-dappled shadows from the *burau* trees along the terrace moved as slowly over her stout figure as she moved at her work. Hearing footsteps, she glanced over her shoulder in my direction.

At that moment a gust of poignant emotion swept across the senses; or, better, stirred the depths of feeling. It was then that the heart rather than the mind told me that Rivnac was gone.

Henriette dropped the broom and sat down on the floor with a solid thump. She hid her face in her hands and remained in that position, making no sound, tears trickling through her fingers. Tahitian women have warm and sensitive hearts. When someone for whom they have deep affection dies, upon first meeting, later, another person associated with the one who is gone, they must weep. Often they put their arms around him and weep on his shoulder. Sometimes they sit down where they are and give way to their feelings, as Henriette did on this occasion.

I took my customary chair to wait until she had had her cry out. I joined her, after a fashion, but mine was the tearless grief that gives so little relief; but that is the way most men weep, if it may be called weeping. It doesn't purge the emotions. I envied Henriette whose tears trickled down the backs of her hands and bare forearms, and dripped from her elbows onto her *pareu*, making it really wet.

She rose slowly to her feet and gave me a forlorn smile as she dried her hands and arms on her *pareu*.

"Why am I crying for that fat man?" she said. "What good does it do?"

Beside the broom lay the little pile of sweepings: sand that had been tracked in, a few beer-bottle caps and some leaves that had blown in from the terrace.

"There's no more Amstel," she said; "but I can give you a bottle of Aorai. It's cold."

Aorai is a local beer, brewed in Papeete. Henriette's "It's

cold" was all that could be said in its favor; nevertheless I ordered a bottle.

She stood by, watching, as I opened the parcel containing the new album of records. "Is it that one?" she asked, as I laid it on the table.

I nodded. "His old records were worn-out. This is a new recording. I bought it in San Francisco."

She opened the cover and glanced mournfully inside. "These are red in the middle. . . . Do you want me to play them?" She glanced at his chair as though half expecting to see him there again. I shook my head.

"We ought to play something for him," she said.

I could see that she would be deeply disappointed if I had not agreed, so I suggested an album of Dvořák's "Slavonic Dances," favorites of Rivnac. I loved them too, and so did Henriette: she could appreciate that kind of music. I selected numbers three and seven that Rivnac had been particularly fond of in certain moods.

Henriette cried some more as we listened, rubbing her eyes with the backs of her hands. She replaced the records in the album and returned it to the shelf amongst the others.

"Well, I'd better get on with my work, but first I'll bring you something to eat."

I told her that I was not hungry but would wait in the lounge until time for the afternoon bus back to Papeete.

"But you ought to eat something," she insisted. "I'll make you some sandwiches to go with the beer." When she had done so she returned to the kitchen, forgetting what she had been doing when I came. The broom and the little pile of sweepings remained in the middle of the floor.

As already explained, Rivnac and I had met, in spirit, twenty years before we were aware of one another's existence. Now, in spirit, I bade him farewell. I lost the sense of his presence there beside me. Tahiti vanished, and I heard as though from an infinite distance the ghostly music of the Largo. It was leading him northward, but the road was not my road in Iowa, although something like it. The fields on either side were snow-covered, but instead of being golden in the wan sunlight of a February afternoon they were a wintry gray, and the hour was later. But I could see him in the last faint light of evening, head bowed, hands behind his back, trudging slowly north-ward, leaving behind him the homeland he had so longed to see; that had vanished in so brief a time.

VI. Frisbie of Danger Island

His full name is Robert Dean Frisbie, but among the scattered islands and archipelagoes of Polynesia where he spent the whole of his adult life, he was known, simply, as Ropati, the island variant for the name Robert. I first met him on the island of Tahiti on the day in the early nineteen-twenties when he stepped ashore from the monthly steamer from San Francisco, and the friendship then begun lasted until the day of his death in November 1948. I still have in mind a clear picture of Frisbie as he stood that morning, a portable typewriter in one hand and a camera in the other, letting his glance travel slowly along the line of small vessels moored by the sea wall. He gave a sigh of content and said, "This is just what I hoped it would be."

I pointed out how pretty the street bordering the waterfront looked in the early morning light. He glanced briefly at it as though he had not noticed before that a town was there; evidently he was not interested in it. "I mean," he said, "it's what I hoped it would be as a jumping-off place. All these ships . . . I suppose you can go almost anywhere from here?"

We walked the length of the waterfront and he paused to examine every kind of small craft lying there — copra schooners, Low Island cutters, fishing boats — with an air of wistful

[154]

eagerness; he had eyes for nothing else. I asked whether he had a boat of his own. "No," he said, glumly, "but . . . I'm going to. I expect to build it myself." A happy light came into his eyes as he spoke of his "little ship." She was to be thirty-six feet over all, broad beamed . . . he went on telling me about her rig, dimensions, how she was to be fitted inside — everything. He dreamed it into existence there and then; saw it moored by the sea wall. It was as though he were just ready to go aboard and head for the open sea.

"She's sturdy," he said. "Nothing for speed but that doesn't matter. I'm in no hurry. And the important thing is that I can handle her myself."

She was to be his home for the rest of his life, he said. He planned to carry it with him wherever he went, as a hermit crab carries its shell, except that the shell was to carry him. He spoke with such assurance that I could almost believe the boat was there, waiting for him to come aboard. "I read somewhere that there are thirty thousand islands in the Pacific. Do you suppose that's true? Not that I expect to visit all of them; only the loneliest ones."

We had lunch together at the Hotel Tiaré, and by the time we'd finished I realized that my companion was no "type." I didn't quite know what to make of him. He appeared to be a combination of widely different personalities. One would have said that several Frisbies of different ages were sitting there, quarreling and contradicting one another. At this first meeting the one most in evidence was a dreamer who had something of a child's gift for make-believe. He told me of his great dream in which the dream of the boat was only the means to an end. It was, surely, a strange one for a young man to cling to in alternating moods of hope and despair.

[155]

After lunch we went to a little park on the waterfront and sat there talking throughout the afternoon. Or, rather, Frisbie talked and I listened, putting in an occasional remark. I could see that he felt the need to unburden himself; to discuss his plans and hopes and dreams with a sympathetic listener whose interest would give him encouragement, and perhaps subdue the voices of the more clear-sighted Ropatis with whom the dreamer had long contended.

He spoke of the chance that had made it possible for him to reach this "jumping-off place" in the mid-Pacific. When World War I ended he was in an infantry training camp in California. He loathed army life, not being cut out for a regimented existence. His lungs had always been weak and camp life did nothing to improve the condition. He would have been invalided out of the service had the war not ended when it did. At his last medical examination the doctor told him that unless he was extremely careful his prospect was that of a bed in a t.b. sanatorium. He felt unreasonably bitter toward Uncle Sam, as though he were responsible for the state of his health; and so he applied for, and was granted, a pension — $100 per month. This would take care of living expenses, but if he were to carry out his plan for building the little ship in which he was to spend his life wandering in the Pacific, he would have to find a job so that he could earn the money for building her. He had found just what he wanted. An American newspaper syndicate gave him a roving commission in the Pacific. He was to go where he pleased, taking photographs of picturesque island scenes and events. With the photographs he was to send little one-page stories describing them.

"There is no salary attached," he went on. "I'm to be paid according to the amount of work I turn in and how many Sunday newspapers buy my stuff. I expect to earn at least $100 per month, and every penny of this is to be saved for the boat. When I have it I mean to chuck the job. And then . . ."

His dream was to become a writer, and a particular kind of writer. "I don't care how long it takes me," he said. "I will work for years, all my life if necessary, to write my one book. I can live on my pension until I have it finished. But in the end I hope to make a name for myself, in my one small field."

"And what is that?" I asked.

He hesitated for a moment; then he replied, "Myself. It's a small enough field when you think of the millions of human beings on the earth. But looked at in another way, how vast it is, if I can really learn to explore it. It's never been done, this kind of research; I mean, not honestly done. There is glorious old Montaigne, of course: his essays were all in the field of self-exploration, but my approach will be from a different angle. The others who have tried it, Rousseau among them, were charlatans. They thought too much of themselves to understand themselves. I think nothing of myself; that's why I hope to succeed."

He was not aware of the contradictory nature of his statement and I didn't point it out to him. I was astonished, to say the least, to hear this twenty-year-old talk so confidently of a task in which no one, however honest, however gifted, could hope to succeed. He mapped out the plan of his life which would be directed toward and culminate in the great work, to be completed, he hoped, in twenty-five years. Solitude was, of course, essential; he must be alone with himself most of the time, hence the one-man ship in which he was to visit the loneliest of islands. Contemplation of this fact made him a little uneasy. He loved solitude, but he also loved a certain

[157]

amount of companionship. However, it was necessary that he should forgo the latter, probably for years at a time, and he believed that he had the courage to do so.

I didn't know what to say, so I remained silent while Frisbie was telling me this. It was as though he were talking to himself rather than to me. Presently he broke off to give me an anxious look.

"Do you think I'm a complete idiot?" he asked. "It may be true. I've had no education except what I have picked up for myself by reading. I dream of writing this great book and I can't even spell properly, to say nothing of writing the King's English."

He sat with his chin in his hands, a picture of gloom. When I came to know him better I discovered that sudden changes of mood from radiant hope to the deepest discouragement were common with him, and there would be a remarkable physical change as well. With the light gone from his eyes he would look ten years older. I wanted to encourage him but I didn't know how to go about it.

Presently I said, "If it means so much to you, why not try it? If you failed, would that be such a tragedy?"

"To me, it would."

"I don't see why," I replied. "You might find the result quite otherwise. You might be led off on another track toward something you could do really well."

"What kind of thing?" he asked.

"Well, something allied, at least, to what you hoped to do. The subject could still be yourself, but you would not attempt to be a competent witness. Who could hope to be that, in exploring one's self?"

The look of misery changed to one of mere woefulness.

"I'm not ready to admit that it can't be done. Surely, my great desire to be honest would count for something? I know this: if I were to catch myself indulging in any half-conscious trickery I would drop the work at once. The last thing in the world I want to do is to fool myself."

"In that case," I said, "why not go ahead?"

"I've got to," he replied. "The only thing is, if I do fail, it will be such a bitter disappointment."

I was tempted to say that any man who believed that he could tell the complete truth about himself had a fatal defect of vision to start with, but it seemed likely that he would soon discover this for himself.

He gave me a forlorn account of the schools he had attended. His father, he said, was a gentle kindly man, but without depth of character or a will of his own. All his life he had searched for a religious faith to cling to.

"And where do you suppose he looked for it? Among the cranks and frauds who make a business of supplying 'faiths' for profit to just such people as my dad. He went from one sect to another, and I was dragged along with him, attending the kind of private schools such people keep. Finally we landed in Southern California. It was heaven for my father, a dozen varieties of heaven; but it was hell for me."

No more need be said of that first meeting with Frisbie, and I will pass briefly over the next seven years of his life. He spent most of this time on Tahiti, with visits to some of the neighboring islands. And he didn't build the boat.

He found a place to live on a lonely stretch of beach in the district of Papéari, thirty-five miles from the town of Papeete, built himself a small house of bamboo and palm-frond thatch, and, in a very halfhearted fashion as it seemed to me, set about his task of self-exploration. In fact, he seemed to have all but forgotten that ambitious project. He may have realized that he was too young even to attempt it at that time, and that more experience at living was needed, first. However this may be, he rarely alluded to the dream of the book that he had outlined to me so hopefully at the time of our first meeting; but the dream of the boat-building was never forgotten.

There were Tahitians living nearby, simple kindly folk who rarely leave their district and keep to the old native ways. They liked Ropati and he liked them, and in a very short time he was speaking the native language with ease. The more he saw of their free, uninhibited manner of living, the lack of moral restraints which determine the surface conduct of "civilized" folk, the more convinced he became that their way of life was wholly admirable, one to be emulated. Whenever he spoke of "civilization" he placed unseen quotation marks around the word. What he particularly admired in the natives was their lack of hypocrisy in their personal and social relations. He considered the loss of it and the necessity for losing it a heavy price to pay for being "civilized."

The only other white man then living on that part of the island was an American from New England, a former professor of electrical engineering at a famous technical school in the East. He was a man of the highest moral standards who believed in maintaining them no matter where he lived. Having met Frisbie and learned of his plan for voyaging westward in a boat of his own, he offered to teach him navigation. Frisbie eagerly accepted the offer. That he had undeveloped capabilities is evidenced by the fact that, without previous training in mathematics, he mastered trigonometry and the art of navigation in astonishingly quick time.

His teacher, the professor, was, as I have said, a man of the highest moral character. He did not attempt in any way, except by example, to impose his own standard of conduct upon his native neighbors, but he could not easily overlook or forgive, in another white man, any departure from what he considered proper behavior. Frisbie's easy mastery of navigation had won his high regard, but he was deeply shocked when he discovered that the young man had "gone native" with a vengeance. He had taken a native mistress and seemed determined to forget that he had ever lived as a white man, except for the fact that he sometimes got drunk on his visits to Papeete. The professor was no teetotaler, but he had nothing but contempt for a man who abused alcohol. Had it been just any young man he would have dropped his acquaintance, but his regard for Frisbie made it necessary for him to admonish his pupil, quietly, but firmly and repeatedly. He was horrified at the thought that this young man, so likable, and gifted with undeveloped personal abilities of a high order, was on the road to becoming a combination white Kanaka and beachcomber. It was his duty to bring him to his senses before it was too late.

This brought to the fore the reckless, defiant Frisbie who could not and would not be lectured to. A few others as well lost no opportunity in pointing out to the defiant one that he was going to the dogs. The result was that Frisbie went out of his way to shock his critics. He wanted them to believe that going to the dogs, in the European or American sense of the term, was his way toward personal salvation. He was by no means an alcoholic, but he was so highly strung that two rum punches could make him drunk: a physiological rather than a moral defect, as it seemed to me. His real friends avoided him on such occasions, for alcohol had an immediate and unfortunate effect upon him. The dreamer, with his high enthusiasms — which, despite his natural modesty, made him believe, or hope, that the most glorious dreams might be realized — became a braggart and a boaster. *In Vino Veritas* was not true in his case. His words and actions when drunk belied his true character.

Many a happy day we spent together, in the mountains, or paddling in his outrigger canoe along the lagoons bordering his side of the island. He loved his canoe as though it were a living thing, but it was not the little ship that he still dreamed of and planned for. That was to come. Saving for it was a much harder task than dreaming it into existence. Somehow, the newspaper syndicate job had ended. I believe that it failed to hold his interest, despite the fact that it was to provide the money for building the boat. I realized by this time that he must have inherited something of his father's instability of character, but there was nothing unstable in his character as a friend. He had many acquaintances by this time but few friends, and a few were all he wanted. He was firmly of the opinion that no man could have more than half-a-dozen real friends.

Gradually he collected a small library, around two hundred volumes: Montaigne, Swinburne, both the prose and the poetry, George Borrow, François Villon, in translation, Dante's *Inferno,* in the Cary translation, Mungo Park's *Travels,* some of George Meredith's novels, Charles Lamb, both the *Essays* and the *Letters,* and miscellaneous volumes, most of them books to live with. But his great passion was for De Quincey; he all but worshiped him. A corollary to the dream had been that the style for the Book must be as unusual as he hoped the contents would be. De Quincey was the great master of style, he thought, but he had no intention of imitating him or anyone else. He hoped, eventually, to discover his own style, and this was, sometimes, the explanation he gave for his long sojourn on Tahiti. He must read and read to make up for lost opportunity and to destroy the effect which his fad-and-cult-tainted boyhood education had had upon his mind.

He borrowed many volumes from my library, and I remember what a find Logan Pearsall Smith's *Trivia* seemed to be for him, at first. There, he thought, was another explorer of Self: a man who could look within and write with complete detachment of what he discovered. And what miracles of condensation he could perform! A paragraph sufficed to lay bare great areas. *Trivia* renewed, temporarily at least, enthusiasm for his own projected work. But, later, he revised his opinion of *Trivia*. It was what the name implied: mere notes and comments of no great importance, and written for effect by a man who was no true explorer of self, but, rather, a dilettante and a seeker after perfection in the use of words.

Seven years is a long time, and Ropati the dreamer sickened perceptibly during the latter part of it. Nevertheless, I often found myself preferring the more robust, common-sense Ropati whose clearness of vision with respect to their composite nature was of a kind that the first was wholly unaware of. The two were often in conflict, but the dreamer still held, with a kind of faint earnestness, to his plan for writing the great work. This was the situation at the time when, at last,

Frisbie decided to start on his wanderings. One reason for the decision was, I believe, that he agreed, secretly, with some of his critics that he was becoming, or had become, a mere loafer and drifter. He still planned to make an effort to write the Book. "If I can't," he said, gloomily, "what is there left for me? I have no imagination in the high sense. I can't create. I can write only of what I see and hear — of matters out of my own experience." I again suggested that he would be writing about himself in relation to his environment, and that he might find more real satisfaction in doing so than in his hazardous Quest for the absolute Self.

His farewell to his Tahiti friends was waved, not from the "little boat," but from the deck of a copra schooner bound for the Leeward Islands. From there he went on to Rarotonga, in the Cook Islands. Later I received a long letter written from the lagoon island of Puka Puka, or Danger Island, to give it its English name, one of the loneliest atolls in the Pacific. He was in heaven and he meant to remain there, for good. He had been given a job running a trading station for A. B. Donald & Company, whose schooner visited the island once or twice a year. We corresponded regularly although our letters could be received only at long intervals. Some of the most interesting of Frisbie's letters, written during the first four years of his sojourn on Puka, have been lost. During this time he wrote a story of his life on the island which was published under the title *The Book of Puka Puka*. It was not *the* Book, dreamed of for so long. That was never again mentioned.

He fell in love with and married Nga, a Puka Puka girl of sixteen who knew nothing of life beyond that small palm-clad circle of land. It was a happy marriage and Nga became the mother of his five children. I will now quote from letters received from Frisbie during the years from 1934 until his death, fourteen years later.

PUKA PUKA
August, 1934

DEAR HALL: —

What a lonely, lost, forgotten place this is! Its detachment from the outside world is sometimes staggering, but it doesn't numb me as it once did. I can sink into the Puka Puka habit of mind and drift serenely through the days without a thought of anything but food and the life on this microscopic world in itself.

I wish you were here so we could talk about dreams. I've been having a dream life such as I've never known before; long complete things like novels, with definite beginnings and ends. Nga is a little dear. She works hard, feeds her man, and makes her sisters help take care of the babies.

I am enjoying tremendously the letters of Joseph Conrad, but I can't help thinking that he must have been a bit of a fraud. The way he eulogizes over his friends' work — Cunninghame Graham's for example — does not ring true to me. If Graham's books are as fine as Conrad makes them out to be I would like to read one or two. This is unfair, of course, for I know nothing about the gent.

I will return your *Marriage of Loti* some day. I can't believe that you are in a hurry for it, and you may be sure that I won't steal it. What sentimental rubbish! If it wasn't for the fine imagery and some of the descriptive passages it would be no better than my *Téanau*. "My dear little Rarahu! Sweet flower of the Delicious Isle! . . . And she loved me as dearly as her little savage heart could love." A French naval officer with chronic satari-

[165]

asis slobbering over "a bit of stuff" he probably picked up on the Tahiti waterfront. Forgive the coarseness, but this is what I think of Loti's book. I hope it teaches me to give a wide berth to this kind of writing in the future.

PUKA PUKA
November 25th, 1934

I don't think I can recapture the mood for another book about Puka Puka. I consider various approaches. I was thinking, not seriously, of course, of writing some imaginary reports by Puka Pukans to be read before the island Ethnological Society. It would be amusing to imagine a group of Puka Puka anthropologists, ethnologists and the like, who visit the U.S.A. and return to deliver a series of lectures on their findings. They would tell, for example, of the absurd aversion of the Americans to having the Puka Pukans dig up the bones of George Washington or Thomas Jefferson; and how they refused them permission to make excavations in the Arlington cemetery for the purpose of carrying away the bones of other prominent Americans for measurement and study.

The idea was suggested to me because two odd *manuwiri* have recently arrived at Puka Puka: a Doctor B——, Ph.D., and his wife, an A.B. They are here under the auspices of Yale and the Bishop Museum, and will stay six months whether they want to or not. They landed with hundreds of cases of canned food and notebooks by the bale, and are now installed in Pain-in-the-Head's house in Yato Village, a mile from my house. They, of course, would like to dig up the bones of ancient Puka Pukans, measure and maul them over and carry them away, together with any trinkets they might find in

[166]

the graves. Naturally, the living Puka Pukans object to this, for they honor their ancestors just as we do ours. But think how often the thing has been done by European and American scientists on islands scattered all over the Pacific.

I'm wondering if the B——s aren't going a little bughouse. The other day Mrs. B—— said to me: "Will you please describe to me the exact technique of copulation among these islanders?" I wonder what kind of a response my hypothetical Puka Pukan anthropologist would get from a member of the Yale faculty if he were to ask him to describe the technique of copulation among his colleagues, male and female?

However, the B——s are nice people, though completely out of place here. Among their cases of preserved food, yeast tablets and tropical gear, they have a number of fine books. For the past two weeks I have had the inestimable pleasure of reading Doughty's *Arabia Deserta.* If only I could write like that! Have you read it? If not, you have days, weeks of solid enjoyment ahead.

The children are thriving. Mrs. B—— says that Whiskey Johnny [his daughter, Florence] is an Electra, and Dr. B—— says I should teach her to be bilingual. But Johnny does very well as she is. She has innocently learned all the dirty words in Puka Pukan and uses them indiscriminately before papa and old Heathen William alike. We spend most of our time on the uninhabited islet of Ko, across the lagoon, and now that the B——s are here we will go oftener still. We are well and hearty despite honest poverty. I receive occasional letters from Tahiti "friends" who hope that I am now rehabilitated. Why is it that such busybodies cannot understand that a man has the right to live his own life? By admonishing him they admit that the admonisher is a very fine fellow, much better than the admonished.

I have written my tenth book — that is, in manuscript. The old urge has kept me going despite apathetic publishers and public. I wonder if I should ever have attempted to write?

As usual, life is centered around one thing: my ten-ton cutter. I feel closer to it now than ever before. Perhaps in a few months I may be able to fit a few ribs on the fine *tamau* keel I have laid.

June, 1935

I have finished *A Child of Tahiti.* You will like it but probably no one else. God knows when my boat will be finished, but if ever I sell anything again every penny of the money will go to the cutter. . . .

I can't make this letter cheerful so I'd better stop. I have been sober since December, 1933. Two or three bottles of beer at intervals of six months when the schooner comes; not another drop. I can't see that it has helped my writing any. It's simply hell to pour your life's blood into your work and have it come to nothing. I wonder if I'll ever learn that I'm not a genius? My cutter is to be named *Escape.*

At times Frisbie longed to get away from Puka Puka. There were six hundred inhabitants living in three villages on the main islet which was little more than a mile wide either way. The closeness of contact with his neighbors was hard to bear and he would take refuge on one or the other of two small islets at the opposite end of the lagoon. These were uninhabited except at the times when the people went there to make copra. Matauea Point on Ko Islet was his favorite retreat. He would go there, sometimes alone, more often with his wife and children, for he loved having them with him. His dream at this time — as soon as his boat was built — was to sail with his family to the uninhabited island of Suvarrow, about five hundred miles east of Apia, Samoa, where he hoped to remain for the rest of his life.

June 3rd, 1936

I have underlined the date. It is eight months and three days from October 1st, 1935, when we last had news from the world. Do you remember your plan for An Adventure in Solitude? You wanted it to be a spiritual adventure on an uninhabited island; to discover what the effect would be of six months or a year of complete isolation from all other human beings. You said that you would take plenty of food so that you would have to spend no time providing for the needs of the body. I scoffed at your notion of taking food, but after four solid months of living on coconuts and fish, with taro twice per week, I see your point of view.

We are all becoming a little mad, here, waiting for the schooner. Every time a child shouts or a man whoops we are startled into excited tension, believing it is the long awaited "Sail ho!" Four months ago we used up the last of our flour, rice and sugar. My soap for three months has been a handful of ashes while my clothes simply went unwashed. The last match was used two months ago, but I am getting boy-scoutishly clever at making fire by friction. My lamp is a jar of coconut oil with a wick of cotton wool floating in it on a cork. It makes a fair light but not good enough to read by. Tobacco, of course, is gone long since. I pared or shaved the bowls of my old pipes and smoked the shavings. After that I went bughouse until the nicotine was cleaned out of my system, but now I manage tolerably. This kind of living is all right for a time, but bad for months on end. I will not sneer when you take abundant supplies for your Adventure in Solitude.

Oddly enough, I find myself craving a little news from the outside world. Also, I wish to know whether or not my Tahiti book has been accepted. I read the carbon copy a few days ago and decided that it richly deserved the garbage can. My eleventh book, *Unconventional Journey,* is much better. I have been working on it to the limit of my capacity and it is nearly finished.

During six of these months I have been living with Nga and the children on uninhabited Ko Islet. And there I have come under the influence of Marcel Proust. He has become a second master for me and has profoundly affected my conception of Literature. I have read my two volumes, *Swan's Way* and *The Guermantes Way,* over and over again. I read every sentence slowly, think about it, analyze it, often learn it by heart. I am dumbfounded. This kind of writing is something entirely new to me. His philosophy and his outlook on life are not worth bothering about, but his manner of writing! Give me a superlative — a dozen! A discarded mistress walks along by the river "drawing from her submissive fingers long gloves of a precious, useless charm." Maybe I'm just nutty from too much Puka Puka, but sentences like this seem so perfectly what they should be. I have read my two volumes five or six times and am waiting for the schooner to bring me the others. Puka Puka is the place to read him, particularly Ko Islet where I spend three quarters of my time.

My children are in fine health. I now have four. The

last one, Elaine Metua (Alkali Ike), was born the 29th of last November. I hope to take Whiskey Johnny (Florence) to Honolulu at the end of this year. Now that I have this beloved daughter growing up I realize what a depraved place Puka Puka is. I have had a singular change of heart in my attitude about it. The natural depravity of the Puka Pukans doesn't interest me any more; it disgusts me. I have discovered that I am losing my craving for liquor. I simply don't want it. All of this because of the salutary influence of my children, including this latest baby daughter. Curses! What stupidity!

Hall, what kind of a letter is this? But remember that my brain is fagged after a long period of intense concentration, and that I have no tobacco. But I know that when the schooner comes — if it ever comes — there will be no time to write anything but a note.

July 10th, 1936. Still no ship.

August 15th, 1936. The schooner is here. I have learned that *A Child of Tahiti* has been rejected. The manuscript I am working on now will probably meet the same fate.

Knowing Frisbie so well, I also knew what bitter disappointment was covered by the brief statement concerning the fate of his latest manuscript. His remark, quoted earlier, about pouring his heart's blood into his work was true, I think; at least he persuaded himself that he was doing so. The tragedy was that in his own case he never learned to distinguish good work from bad, or so it seemed to me at that time. He had a fine appreciation of literature in the high sense, but, somehow, this could not teach him to be a judge of his own work. Or it may have been that, after working so hard and so long on a manuscript, he was afraid to examine it critically lest he should decide that it was all bad. To read some great book for the first time was, with him, in the nature of a religious experience: he would be lifted out of himself and above himself. And then Ropati, the dreamer, would whisper: "You see? That's how it's done. Take courage! The fact that you are so inspired and uplifted by what you read proves that you have qualities in your own nature akin to those of the masters. Develop them. You have much to learn and a weary way to go, but look ahead — far ahead! Can't you see the dream of what you so long to be taking form and substance; becoming reality at last?"

And Ropati's spirit would again be kindled and quickened. Grimly but hopefully he would set to work once more, writing, writing with feverish energy, and sometimes enthusiasm would carry him through to the end. Then, usually, came disillusionment and despair and he would be too sick at heart to begin all over again. In one of his letters written from his beloved Matauea Point on Ko Islet, he wrote:

> I see clearly now what a terrible handicap it is to be completely cut off from contact with other men interested in writing. If I were a great genius it wouldn't matter, but I'm only a plain damn fool trying to make a silk purse out of a sow's ear. You are right: I'm a poor judge of my own work, worse than I used to be. One reason for that is that I've lived here too long. I not only speak Puka Pukan and nothing else, but I think Puka Pukan. You couldn't even imagine the world they live in. There is a lot to be said for it, and if I could only kill this cursed desire to write I could be happy in it. How could you expect a man who writes in English and thinks in Puka Pukan to be able to know what kind of work he is doing?

[172]

My old friend, William the Heathen, is the only critic I've got. He is now a very old man but still keeps healthy. In his early days he made several voyages in American whalers and is proud of the fact that he hasn't forgotten the English he learned at that time.

He came over the other day to visit me. I was writing and kept on with it, so William sat down nearby and went into the coma that comes so easy to a native. His eyes were open but his mind, so called, was a complete blank. Finally I stirred him out of it. "William, listen to this!" He gave me a kind of vacant leer. I waited until he'd come back to the Puka Puka state of consciousness and then read him a paragraph of what I'd just been writing — in English, of course. "How do you like that, William?" He likes to be reminded that we are "fellow Americans," and he fairly beamed this time.

"Whassa matter, you, Ropati cowboy? You me spik English! Goddam! Me no Puka Puka kanaka! What ta hell! Me whaler-man! Me spik too much English!"

This was William's only comment on the immortal paragraph. What he may have meant was that I write too much English. Lord knows I do, if it deserves to be called English.

William the Heathen, as he calls him, acted as a kind of safety valve for Frisbie. When he was "fed up to the ears" with native life which the dreamer liked to idealize, the clear-sighted practical Ropati would take over and call in old William, who told him ribald tales of his youth and was a living *Who's Who* with respect to the character of all his fellow Puka Pukans. Frisbie had a real affection for old William who was of the Earth, earthy. He never tired of his company and when he was in a dark mood, a talk with William usually brought him out of it. The above letter in which he comments upon William the literary critic continues:

Three weeks ago I finished my *Unconventional Journey*. It runs to ninety thousand words of cleaned and perfumed tripe. It reads all right for about fifty pages, but if you can read a hundred you'll be fed up. One year and one month of solid hard work, and during the whole of the time, absolute sobriety. When you told me I'd have my boat if I worked hard for a year and kept sober, you were all wrong. I've been sober since January, 1934 — three years — and the result has been three articles accepted by the *Atlantic Monthly*. If only you would say: "Ropati, stop being a fool! You're no writer and never will be." Instead of that you prod me on.

But I don't really mind the prodding; I could stand a lot more of it. Hall, listen to this. I had a letter from Edward Weeks of the *Atlantic* in which he said they would be delighted to use two of my stories: "Uninhabited Island," and "The Grandpapa of All the Fishes." And as if that weren't enough encouragement for a starving man, he also said: "It is a delicious mixture of present and past. . . . There are months when the *Atlantic* cries aloud for good graphic humor such as this. . . . 'Uninhabited Island' builds up a kind of dream picture that Coleridge would have loved. . . . My interest in your work began with the first Puka Puka articles and has never wavered."

Can you imagine what this means to me? Fifty-four words — count 'em — but I can live on them for months, years, if necessary. Probably I'll have to. Life on Puka Puka has taught me how to live on short rations. I use ashes to wash with when the soap gives out, and ashes had been my principal diet for the inner man until Weeks's letter came. He may want to eat his words, later, but he can't. They're my emergency rations.

Not later than the middle of 1937 I'm going to take the family to Aitutaki, and there I will make one more attempt to build my boat; there is some fine timber on Aitutaki. Years roll by, Hall Tané. Think of it! I'm forty now. If I don't manage to build my boat pretty soon I'm going to throw my typewriter into the lagoon and settle down permanently to nothing but my trading job. That means failure. I know it. And failure is synonymous with dissipation and death.

But I can't allow myself to think of that. As old William might tell me — "Whassa matter, you, Ropati cowboy? What ta hell! You no Puka Puka kanaka! You writerman!" One thing I know: I build too many dream pictures of my boat. Now I've got to build a real one.

The fact that he did not yet have his boat after seventeen years of dreaming of it and planning for it was, to Frisbie, evidence of failure that could neither be wished away nor explained away. Another man with no better opportunities than his own would have had it long since. He reproached himself for having become a typical low-caste Kanaka; the kind of man who will start building for himself a coral-lime dwelling and leave it unfinished at the time of his death. It was what he had wanted more than anything else in the world. And now his children were of an age when they could sail with him. The boat would be the family home in which they could wander all over the Pacific. He resolved once more that the boat would be a reality before another year had passed.

FRISBIE OF DANGER ISLAND

Old friend, keep a buzzard's eye peeled for an essay by Robert Dean Frisbie called, "Javan Moonlight on the Dawn." It is a part of my novel, *Javan Moonlight,* which is a wholly different kind of *Book of Puka Puka.* There is a story running through and it goes to 150,000 words — perfect continuity, biographical suspense, and a whale of a climax. The thing is too big for me; it has gotten out of hand. By the time I was halfway through I'd forgotten how it started. If only I could be sure I'm on the right track this time. What is so discouraging is being alone here and having only old Heathen William for a critic.

I now have the full set of Marcel Proust and am reading him slowly, with infinite delight. My style is being affected by him, but whether for better or worse I can't tell. He has taught me how to express difficult abstractions which formerly I avoided, and unusual ways of sentence building. He is a constant revelation to me, or it may be Scott Moncrief, his translator and interpreter, who is teaching me things.

Despite the extreme isolation of Puka Puka and the primitive conditions of living there, Frisbie took pride in the fact that he could so easily adapt himself to them. In this same letter he describes the circumstances under which his youngest child was born.

A week ago Nga presented me with another daughter. — Ngatokoruaimatauea [Nga-at-Matauea]. We won't address her by the full name in ordinary conversation. She was born at Matauea Point on Ko Islet. Nga and I were alone here, but I had arranged for Heathen William to come over with the midwife to help me when the time came. Well, on the night of September 30th her pains began, so I lit torches and signaled to the village, four miles away. Then I lay on the beach near our little house, thinking it would be twenty-four hours or so before anything happened. I was dozing when Nga's groans wakened me. I rushed into the house, arriving about a minute before Ngatokoruaimatauea did. There was no hot water, no nothing; however I managed to do all the necessary things. Now a week has passed and mother and baby seem quite all right in spite of the lack of hospital, husbands' waiting-room, obstetrician, nurses, anaesthetics, blood tests, prenatal care, post-natal care, etc., etc. And no post-natal hospital, doctor's and nurses' bills to come. Old William and the midwife arrived three hours too late. "Goddam, Ropati cowboy! You got pickaninny come too bloody soon!"

William didn't explain the reason for the delay, but knowing how the native mind works I can explain it myself. Imagine William asleep on the beach of the village island. He wakes up and sees the light of my signal torch. The dots that follow, as William communes with himself, represent intervals of from five to fifteen minutes.

"There's a light on Ko. . . . Wonder who's over there? . . . Maybe it's Ropati cowboy. . . . Maybe Nga is with him. . . . Oh, yes, I remember now, she *is* with him. . . . Wasn't she going to have a baby? . . . Yes, that's right. She was. . . . And Ropati asked me to bring the midwife over when I saw his signal. . . . I'll go and find her."

It would take nearly as long for William to rouse the midwife as it did to rouse himself.

In another letter written at about this time Frisbie described the great event of the year at Puka Puka: the arrival of A. B. Donald's schooner and the native reaction to it.

I have told you how anxious we Puka Pukans are to see the ship when it is long overdo. I will now tell you how that anxiety displays itself. Captain Viggo's, or Andy's schooner, after a six, seven, or eight months' absence, appears over the horizon. We see it approaching over the sea that has been empty for so long. It is in plain sight all the way. Now it is just beyond the reef, standing off and on, waiting for us. We are all gathered on the beach, some standing, some sitting, staring at the ship. Not in astonishment — we haven't reached that point. We see the ship but we don't know it's there yet. Can you blame us? The sea has been empty for so long and our minds work so slowly that we have to wait until the idea, "Ship," glimmers up and comes to focus on the surface of consciousness. Meanwhile the schooner is idling back and forth waiting for us. Viggo or Andy — whichever schooner it is — knows how it is with us and is very patient, but the supercargo — Bates, maybe, or Wilkie — is fuming. The following conversation takes place:

BATES. Andy, look at the bloody fools! Don't they know we're here?

ANDY. Well . . . yes . . . maybe.

BATES. Maybe! They got eyes, ain't they?

ANDY. Well, Bates, you know how it is. They've been a long time without a ship, and . . .

BATES. Then why don't they come out, now we're here? Squattin' on the beach like a lot o' dummies! We been standin' off and on a good half-hour.

ANDY. They'll be along, directly. Anyway, Ropati will.

BATES. Ropati! He's nothing but a bloody kanaka! He's lost what little mind he had.

ANDY. I wouldn't say that, Bates. If you were alone here for months on end the way Ropati is, never seeing a white face . . .

BATES. Me? Here? I wouldn't be such a damn fool!

ANDY. There he comes now.

BATES. Well, it's about time!

In one of my letters I sent Frisbie a copy of some verses I had written about my small daughter, Nancy. Our children made up much of the subject matter of our letters; Ropati boasted about his and I about mine. My two, Conrad and Nancy, were nine and five years old at the time the poem, "The Walk with Nancy," was written. I had had a dream about Nancy, as vivid as it was distressing. The memory of it kept haunting me, and at last I tried to exorcise it by relating the dream in verse.

> We had been walking hand in hand.
> Paradise itself, the land;
> I had no thought or care.
> Nancy was singing "Papio";
> Suddenly I seemed to know
> She was no longer there.

> I felt the chill of coming night.
> Nowhere was the landscape bright;
> The wind began to moan.
> The road sloped steeply down, before;
> Nancy's song I heard no more —
> I was there alone.

I could not halt. I tried, but no,
Faster yet I had to go
Down that forbidding hill.
And all the time I knew that she
Was trying to catch up with me,
Crying as children will

When left behind, alone and lost.
Countless stony fields I crossed;
I could not check my gait.
And then I heard, a world away,
It seemed, from where I could not stay:
"Daddy! Wait! Please wait!"

If ever heart was wrung to hear
The voice of one it loved most dear,
Helpless to reply,
My heart was wrung. If ever man
Tried all that strength and willing can
To halt, that man was I.

I could not even turn my head.
And then I knew that I was dead,
Or just about to be.
Oh, I have tasted bitterness.
I heard the voice grow less, and less,
Of Nancy, calling me.

Had I known the effect these verses were to have upon Frisbie, I would never have sent them. They were to play a strange part in his introspective musings, some of them reflected in his letters. The first time I noticed this was in the following letter written on a dark day in Frisbie's life.

PUKA PUKA
January 23rd, 1938

Andy is here with the *Tagua*. Everything is upside-down ashore. I have only a moment to write before the supercargo comes back. Hall, Nga has tuberculosis and probably won't live longer than a few months. What will I do if she dies? I have not heard from the *Atlantic Monthly* for a solid year. All my *Moonlight* manuscript has been lost. It must have been; otherwise I would have heard something about it. The price of copra has gone to the dogs and the store is to be closed. I was hoping to go to Aitutaki to start building my boat, but that's ended, of course. I don't know what will happen. Nga has wasted away to nothing. If she dies I will be left alone with the children. And if I should die . . . I keep thinking about your dream poem, "The Walk with Nancy." That may happen to my little family, "left behind, alone and lost." No time to write more.

Yours
ROPATI

Needless to say, I was deeply distressed by the news in Frisbie's last brief letter. In earlier letters he had never revealed anxiety about Nga's health, and his only mention of tuberculosis had been in connection with his own susceptibility to it. That, apparently, had ceased to worry him.

I had to wait long for further news. His next letter was dated September 20th, 1938, from Apia, Samoa. A British warship, H.M.S. *Leith*, had called at Puka Puka, and Ropati was given passage with his wife to Apia where she was immediately placed in the Government hospital. Only one of the children, his younger son, "Jakey," went with them. The others

were left with the mother's relatives on Puka Puka. As usual,
Ropati had practically no money. He had his U. S. Veteran's
pension — which had been reduced from $100 to $50 — to live
on. He also had some Adjusted Service bonds which he cashed
to help pay the hospital bills; but he was in a forlorn state,
both morally and financially. His earliest letters from Samoa
were scarcely more than bulletins about Nga's condition, but
I could read between the lines and see how matters stood
with him. For all that he tried to conceal it, heartsickness and
desperation showed through. He had no friends in Samoa but
formed various acquaintanceships. He mentioned with a kind
of woeful humor how they made shift to eat. He listed the acquaintances, and he and Jakey would drop in on one or another of them about mealtime, taking care not to do this too
often.

APIA, SAMOA
October 12th, 1938

After the long dry years on Puka Puka I went on a
spree, got thrown into jail, and the next morning was
fined a pound for inciting to riot. Worry about Nga was
the real cause of it. Having done credit to the well known
reputation of the South Seas trader, I sobered up, have
since remained sober, and shall continue sober.

Nga is now undergoing what is called a pneumo-thorax
treatment, long, tedious and painful, but sometimes successful. Patients in even worse conditions than Nga have
been cured by it. The doctor reckons it will take about
a year, but the latter part of that time she may be able
to live outside of the hospital. I'll be head over heels in
debt, but what of it? I'll do what Governments do —
England, France and the rest — borrow money with no

intention of paying it back. I have telegraphed for my mail which I have not received all this year. When and if it comes I may have a little money.

All plans for building my boat are bitched, of course. Not a hope, now. I worked a solid year on six essays and all were turned down — even "Javan Moonlight on the Dawn." I spent four months on that. However, I'll get by. My main trouble is being so lonely. Isn't it strange that I should still love my wife, after twelve years of married life? What would they think of me in the U.S.A.? In Hollywood — above all, in Reno?

At about this time I received an explanation of the meaning of the title of his essay, "Javan Moonlight on the Dawn." I couldn't make head nor tail of it until he told me that Javan Moonlight was the name of a man (really himself). Frisbie loved strange names for characters, including himself, and the more fanciful they were the better he liked them. I remember that the fictitious name for one of his characters, a real person, was Table Winning, and how he happened to think of it is more than I can guess.

APIA, SAMOA
October 28th, 1938

I got all my mail, a nine-months collection. Not a cent from any manuscript, and not one encouraging remark from anyone. I received eight Government checks of $50 each and turned the whole works over to the Administration as a deposit against Nga's hospitalization; so Jakey and I are without a bean and more or less living on charity. I'm afraid I'm a no-account fellow, Hall. Anyway, I'm a good hand at getting into tight places. But

[183]

there is some chance of Nga's living, and it would be a poor man who would not sacrifice for his wife.

I am reading Pareto's *Mind and Society.* Having lost my own mind I thought maybe Pareto could give me some hints about how to find it again, but I'm afraid there is no hope. Here is a scholar who has the courage to crack a joke and tell a naughty story in a profoundly thought-provoking piece of work. The volumes are full of his own personality. I'm no scholar. Maybe that is why I enjoy his mixture of humor, pathos, cantankerousness, pornography and sound scientific reasoning — at least it seems sound to me. Better read Pareto if you have not yet done so. Otherwise, if ever we meet again, I will floor you with some such remark as: "Hall! Hall! Ease up on those Group-persistence residues!"

Never come to Samoa. You are no longer in the South Seas that we know and love. Everything is different here. The Samoans are the most mercenary people on the face of the Earth. As far as this place is concerned I agree with supercargo Bates: "The South Seas would be all right if we could only get rid of the bloody kanakas!" But I'm obliged to admit that I am in no position to judge either places or people fairly just now.

APIA, WESTERN SAMOA
November 4th, 1938

Do you mind if I talk about my boat? You are wrong in thinking that a boat such as I want is more expensive than travel by tramp steamer. The best you could hope for on the latter is $4 per day, plus personal expenses such as clothes, laundry, shore excursions, etc. Now for the little boat I have in mind, $100 per month would be ample for upkeep, sails, everything. I know; I have worked it out with great care. Moreover, when a man has no money to sail his boat he can always take it to such an island as Suvarrow and lie low until his funds accumulate. He must paint her twice a year; there are no other necessary expenses. For my needs, a little boat of ten tons is just right, and the only thing worth working for. Lord! When I start on this subject I don't want to stop. I'd like to write on and on; even writing about it gives me pleasure. There is *not a day* that I don't, literally, spend hours dreaming about my boat. I know how many nails are going into it. I know exactly how I will fit every block and eyebolt. I know where the priming-needle for the galley stove will be kept. Now, Hall, you ought to know me better than to suppose I might like to travel on tramp steamers. My boat is to be my home, but this home will have the advantage of mobility. When I am broke and in trouble I will simply up-anchor and sail to Suvarrow, or Canton Island, or Hull Island, or Marie Island. There I will hole-in for a long period, wait for hard times to pass and for a little money to accumulate. You needn't tell me that a ten or twelve-ton boat would provide pretty close quarters for me and the family. I know that; but we could manage while sailing from one island to another where I would make headquarters. Then I would leave the other members of the family behind and make a voyage with my beloved Whiskey Johnny, come back later and take one of the other kids.

Dreaming about the boat was a great resource to him at this time. He had nothing to do but wait until he could know whether his wife was to live or die. His visits to the hospital were necessarily brief because of her condition, and when there he could do little more than look at Nga; it was impossible to talk with her. He could not work, and the long days and nights had to be gotten through with somehow. I gathered that the resolve to remain sober was not strictly adhered to, which is scarcely to be wondered at, under the circumstances. He took walks into the country with Jakey. He saw Vailima — from the outside — the former home of Robert Louis Stevenson, now the home of the Resident Commissioner of Western Samoa. Inevitably, there were some sad and rather bitter reflections as he compared the circumstances of R.L.S., the tubercular but world-famous and affluent author, with those of R.D.F., the penniless husband of a tubercular wife, author of so many rejected manuscripts. He had not much longer to wait to learn what Nga's fate was to be.

APIA, SAMOA
December 5th, 1938

Two weeks ago I was up in the mountains on a banana plantation, stopping with an ex-Navy man named Harrington. One night the hospital ambulance drove up to the door. The driver told me that the chief medical officer wanted to see me at once. At the hospital I learned that something had gone wrong with the pneumo-thorax treatment. Nga was in a critical condition and might die at any moment. She is still in the same condition. The doctors are keeping her alive with strychnine and digitalis. I told them I thought it brutal; she is in continual pain and cannot sleep without morphine. She wants to die and knows there is no hope. One of the doctors replied that I seemed to want her to die. Yes, I said; that's why I brought her here.

There is a motor vessel going to Puka Puka and Nassau

in a few days. I did my best to persuade the doctors to let me take Nga home in this ship. She wants to see the children before she dies. But they said no; she would probably die on the way to Puka Puka. I said that that would not matter; she would certainly die if she remained in Apia. Then they got nasty and said she would remain in Apia as long as they wanted her to. So I will have to bury her in a strange island, among strangers.

Evidently, the doctors relented, for Frisbie's next letter was dated Puka Puka, January 30th, 1939.

I wrote you the 14th of this month, the day that Nga died. Since then there has been a period of stormy weather, so the schooner is still here. I have destroyed the first letter and can now write a saner one.

The night before her death she suffered terribly. We knew the end was near and talked about it. She asked me to be close to her when she died and to hold her in my arms for a little while afterward. It was a long night. Her hands and feet were growing cold and her heart barely fluttering. In the morning her sister, Moloku, came. I sat on the floor with my back against one of the roof-posts, with Nga in my arms. It was the same position we'd been in the year before when we were alone on Ko Islet and our last baby was born. We sent for the children and she cried when she saw them. She said she was too young to die. She wanted to live to see them grown up. Then I sent the children away. In a little while her heart fluttered — I could feel it under my hand — there was a convulsive shudder, her breathing stopped and she relaxed in my arms. She breathed once more, a little sigh of relief, and that was the end. I told Moloku to be quiet so as not to attract the attention of the neighbors; then I held her for half-an-hour as she had asked me to. I closed her eyes and lips, bathed and dressed her and kissed her good-by. The children were sent for again and the relatives. They took Nga away and I did not see her again.

I was only half conscious that she had really gone. The truth came home to me after the burial when I took the children away from the grave. I can find a healthy peace now in visualizing myself dead and in a coffin, lying beside Nga. It *is* a healthy peace because, when imagining one's self dead, there is the live personality standing at one's side, observing. He sees the dead body of himself, and because he sees it there it must be something apart from the observer. This, of course, is casuistry, but it brings me peace nevertheless. I say to myself: if I am not truly able to imagine myself dead, then there can be no death for me, and if there is none for me there is none for Nga. Here I block further thought, feeling that if I carry the argument further its falseness will become evident and peace will be lost.

Yesterday I went to the grave with the children. It was so clean and pretty, like the island itself, covered with white coral gravel and bordered with white coral stones. Johnny brought one of her toy lead horses, made a little hole in the sand, put the horse there and neatly covered it over. She wanted to leave it with Mama; it was her own idea. We sat there for a while talking about Mama. When we left the children called back to her, "*Noo akalelei*" — Sleep prettily — and Johnny reminded her to take good care of the horse.

I try to plan for the future. I think of my boat and a home on Suvarrow Island — just myself and the children. What a fool a man can be! Twenty years of writing without success, the one romance of my life ended, and my children

> trying to catch up with me
> Crying as children will
> When left behind, alone and lost . . .

I hope I am not pitying myself. But I worry about them and what will become of them if anything happens to me.

The dread of dying while his children were still small became, for a time, a kind of obsession with Frisbie, after he lost Nga. I felt troubled by his references to my dream poem about Nancy. He made reality out of this dream except that he was the father concerned and his children were the lost ones. "You shouldn't write such things. They have too painful an effect upon the reader, and there's a morbid streak in me. I feel myself being pushed, or pulled 'down that forbidding hill' by invisible hands."

The next letter was written in a wholly different mood. He had abandoned the literary career for good and all and a great weight seemed to have been lifted from his spirit.

PUKA PUKA
March 25th, 1939

Robert Dean Frisbie, who might have risen to the sunny heights of literature, has sailed off the mountain-side, using his *pareu* for a parachute. The Divine Afflatus has breezed away to parts unknown. A dozen times I have tried to record my impressions of Samoa, but they don't impress, blast them! I have tried to rewrite my novel, *Javan Moonlight*, and I find that it's all moonshine. So I said, "The hell with it!" and would have chucked my typewriter into the lagoon, except for the fact that I needed it to write this letter, telling you how relieved and happy I am; or, if not blissfully happy, reasonably cheerful and optimistic. The future looks sufficiently bright, and regrets for past errors do not weigh unbearably on my conscience. What am I to do about it? If I try to be stern with myself, the sternness vanishes in a froth of relieved chuckles.

I'm fed up with Puka Puka. I must have confused my love for Nga with love for the island. With her death it has lost every atom of its glamour. Even Matauea Point, that I used to think a paradise, is now nothing but an uninteresting sand-bank.

Johnny and I plan to go to Tahiti by the next ship. We have a little money and will try to pick up a small boat, very very cheap; probably a Tuamotu cutter between thirty and thirty-five feet, over all. With a little boat and my $50 per month we should get along handsomely. I am certain that as soon as I have my boat and am able to go where I please, I will be able to do some A No. 1 writing. It is out of the question trying to write any more about Puka Puka. I have, as the reporters say, covered the place. Moreover, as I have said, I now detest the island, and anything I wrote of it would reflect this sour attitude. If I find that I can't make a living by writing I will use the boat as a little trading vessel — a kind of sea peddler. All the islanders like to buy off a ship. They will pay more for a tin of tobacco or a bar of soap or a few yards of dress goods from the trade-room of a ship than they will for the same articles in a store. I remember a peddler in the foothills of California who made his rounds twice a year. He had a covered wagon in which he slept and cooked and had his store. His goods were no better or cheaper than those in the local stores, but people would wait to buy from him. Why? For the novelty of the thing, maybe. Well, I know that I can make a go of being a sea-peddler. I'll stock up in Sydney or Suva or Singapore and then wander all over the Pacific, selling my wares. And think of the literary material I'll gather along with the profits of trading! *The Saga of a South Sea Peddler* — the book is as good as written and I don't see how it could fail to be accepted. I remember what Edward Weeks wrote: "There are months when the *Atlantic* cries aloud for good graphic humor such as this." There will be any amount of it in my *Saga*, and "a delicious mixture of past and present" as well, for I will be voyaging from islands where people are still in the Stone Age to others where they have progressed to the — what? Call it the Film Age.

It's got to be done! My ideal is a boat on exactly the lines of Captain Slocum's *Spray:* 36′ over all, 14′ beam, 4′6″ draft. I wouldn't have a bigger one if you gave it to me with a pink ribbon tied to the bowsprit. If I could have a 10 hp engine I'd be mildly pleased. If I can't, I'll get along without power. After all, Captain Cook, who was as much of a South Sea trader as he was a Navigator, had no engine. Anything Kuki-Tané could do, Ropati-Tané can do.

When I get on this boat subject I enjoy writing. It wouldn't bore me in the least to sit at the typewriter the rest of the day, just gassing about the BOAT.

You'll be saying: What about the family? I've got that all planned. The headquarters will be Suvarrow Island. I think and dream about Suvarrow so much that it ought to be called Frisbie's Island. As I've told you it's uninhabited. I will leave the kids there with Heathen William and Old Mama, his wife, to look after them. Think of the happy life for them! I will take Whiskey Johnny with me for my first trading voyage, then each of the others in turn. The mere thought of this sets me on fire. I'll have to borrow from old William to express my emotion. Goddam! Carramba! Me spik too much English!

I'll be seeing you at Tahiti, maybe before this letter reaches you. Set your mind at rest about one thing: I will not shout a single drink all the time I am in Papeete. But I will, occasionally, accept a drink from you. Only one at a sitting. Never two.

He didn't come. I was looking forward eagerly to his arrival, for we had not met since 1933, when, after his first four-year sojourn on Puka Puka, he had returned to Tahiti, bringing Nga with him. Their third child, Florence, whom he always called "Whiskey Johnny," was born in the Papeete hospital. My daughter, Nancy, was three years old at the time of Whiskey Johnny's birth, and, of course, did not remember her; but she had heard a good deal about her in the meantime from me. She looked forward to meeting Johnny at the time of this proposed 1939 visit, though, naturally, not with the same interest that her dad looked forward to meeting Whiskey Johnny's dad once more. But they didn't come.

Months later I received two letters from Frisbie dated April 1st and May 20th, 1939, but there was no explanation as to why the proposed visit had been abandoned, nor was there any mention of *The Saga of a South Sea Peddler*. That dream, I believe, was born while he was writing the March 25th letter, and it may have faded before he reached the end of it. The letter of May 20th read:

There is a Burns Philp trading-ship here now but she brought no mail, so I have no pleasant letters from you to reply to. However, another ship is expected to call here in July, bringing Viscount Galway, Governor General of New Zealand. I suppose it will be a warship. I have applied for passage on her for Johnny and me to Samoa. If I am turned down I will rig up a reef-boat and Johnny and I will sail it to Pago Pago which is only a little over three hundred miles. From there we will proceed to Honolulu, and maybe on to Tahiti.

In our last mail I received word that Farrar & Rine-hart have accepted *Javan Moonlight*. This is the first volume of a trilogy. The second, *Javan Moonlight's Journey*, I am sending north by this mail. The third will be a grand book called, *The Saga of William the Heathen*. Then, let's hope, I will be able to have my boat.

The apathy displayed in this letter, despite the heartening news that the first part of his *Javan Moonlight* trilogy had been accepted, was sadly revealing. It seemed to me that I could read between the lines Ropati's explanation of the reason why he had not come to Tahiti as planned.

Hall, what a silly thing it was, writing that March letter! I couldn't buy a six-foot skiff, to say nothing of a 35-foot boat. But it did ease my heart a bit to dream that I was just about to do this.

His next letter was written under gloomy circumstances.

We are in the midst of a damnable typhoid epidemic. Five have died so far, and one of my daughters escaped death by a hair's breadth. I am officially in charge of all the cases which now number thirty severe ones and numerous mild ones. Among the cases I have treated all have survived so far; the deaths occurred among those who prefer native doctoring. I can't expect to keep up this record though. The Resident Agent's family are all down on their backs. I suppose I'll contract it by and by, then the island *will* be in a mess. A schooner came here from the Gilbert Islands, picked up twenty-five tons of copra, and left disease and death in its wake. Because of the feeling of horror prevailing here now it is hard to write a pleasant letter. However, I'll try to cheer both of us up by quoting a paragraph from the splendid trilogy now being composed by the unrecognized genius, Ropati-Tané:

"He stretched his long bony limbs luxuriantly, yawned, and glanced southward across the lagoon to the far islet of Ko, where now a faint milky haze seemed to linger above the horizon, definite enough to proclaim the first blush of dawn, but too dim to dull the lustre of alpha and beta Centauri now sinking to the southwest. The stars reminded Javan of the old Polynesian navigators who set their course to Niue by the bearing of the Centauri; and by a natural association of ideas, the navigators reminded him of Toa's branch store and a group of village youths he had advised to go to the war in China.

" 'They are fighting this war in the air,' he recalled having cried, with one of the comprehensive gestures so essential in punctuating the utterances of a South Sea Trader. 'They are winging like frigate birds over the cities, bombing the grandmas and grandpas and the little children. Heroes from all over the world are enlisting in this war to help the Chinese — whose civilization goes back thousands of years — against the Japanese whose civilization began in 1854. You Puka Puka youths know all about that, of course. . . . What? You don't? You have never heard of Commodore Matthew Calbraith

Perry's superb achievement in opening Japan to the influences of Western Civilization? No matter; I'll tell you about that another time. The important thing now is that the Chinese need help. They are not getting it from the governments of England or the United States, but in both of these countries there are a few individual heroes who have not forgotten what civilization in the high sense means. They are going, as airmen, to do what they can to help China. I know — you Puka Puka youths are not airmen, but you are seamen like all of your ancestors. I want you to rig up your double canoes and sail to China. Remember Don Quixote de la Mancha! Remember Cyrano de Bergerac! Be glorious damn fools! There is more honor in that than in being Prime Minister of England or President of the United States. Toa and I have valiant hearts, but we are old wrecks, physically. We would be useless to you. But we can, at least, take care of your private affairs while you are away. We will feed your chickens, work in the taro beds, and do the fishing for your families. And now, prepare for sailing! Not a moment is to be wasted if China is to be saved!' "

How do you like it, Hall? Javan — that's me — is a great dreamer who sees the world as it might be under better management. The *Javan Moonlight* trilogy will be made up as follows:

> Volume I. *The Genesis of a Recluse*
> Volume II. *The Saga of William the Heathen*
> Volume III. *The Revelations of a Recluse*

I have been re-reading *Pitcairn's Island,* hoping to learn the sailor diction of the mutineers and blandly transfer it to my own Volume II — *The Saga of William the Heathen.* You know, when I read this classic — I can flatter when I please — of drunkenness, rape and murder, one sees that the world is only a larger edition of Pitcairn. The mutineers had a little paradise; they could have made of it what they would, and they turn it into a shambles. Whatever man touches he turns into ugliness, misery and death. This is not a very original thought, but it can stand repeating daily, hourly, until he becomes so vividly conscious of it that he turns his thoughts to beauty.

While I am on this subject of the *Bounty* Mutiny, tell me when you next write why Metro-Goldwyn-Mayer have not filmed the Pitcairn part of the tale. Insofar as that goes, why haven't they made a motion-picture trilogy of the story? What a chance! First, the Mutiny part, already done; then *Men Against the Sea* and then *Pitcairn's Island*.

Lord! If only my *Javan Moonlight* trilogy — when and if it is completed — could be sold to the movies! Then I could build my boat. But I won't dream about that. *The Saga of William the Heathen* could be filmed if I can keep from spoiling it with too much introspective musing. But the other two — not a hope. It looks to me now as though my trilogy will run to half a million words.

I've been writing this at odd times. It has kept me from breathing too deeply the misery and fear hanging in the air just now. I haven't heard from the Houghton Mifflin Company. I'll let you know if they write.

I will explain the reference to the Houghton Mifflin Company, the Boston publishers. I had reached the point where I was almost as deeply concerned in the matter of "the little ship" as Frisbie himself. He had been dreaming of it for more than fifteen years, and I wanted, if possible, to help him make the dream come true. And so, during a brief sojourn in the U.S.A., I consulted Mr. Ferris Greenslet, Literary Director of the Houghton Mifflin Company. I knew that Messrs. Houghton Mifflin gave literary "fellowships" to struggling writers, financing them to the extent of $1500 for some piece of work of which they approved. I hoped to get one of these fellowships for Frisbie, but I had not consulted him in advance about it. Mr. Greenslet was sympathetic, but when he asked what kind of book Frisbie might write I couldn't tell him. However, I suggested the possibility of a book of letters under some such title as *The Letters of a South Sea Trader*. Mr. Greenslet thought this might be a suitable project for a fellowship and gave me the application blanks for Frisbie to fill out and return, together with his outline of the contents for the proposed book. I mailed these to Frisbie at once, with an explanatory letter. I felt happy about this and did some dreaming on my own hook. I could see the boat taking form and substance, even to the place where "the priming-needle for the galley stove" was to be kept.

Frisbie was fired by the idea. He filled in the application blanks and sent them to the H–M Company, and, as stated in the above letter, was still waiting to hear from them. And when he did, he was "sunk."

They fill a poor fool with hope, and then write him a brief and extremely chilly note. I can do the book of letters and do it well, but I am not going to waste my time on it when I have no warmer interest in it than Mr. Greenslet shows. But what I think of his attitude and what I think of your devotion to my interests are two different things. I am simply annoyed that Mr. Greenslet should have led you on to putting yourself to a great deal of trouble for my benefit and then write me a brief, cold, and somewhat supercilious letter.

Evidently, this got his dander up. He decided to write the letters anyway, and I first heard of them about six months later.

I have just finished 130,000 words in letters. That damned book that you hatched is written. It is a masterpiece. It recaptures all the youthful enthusiasm of *The Book of Puka Puka,* but does a better job of it. I am not sending it to you or the publishers by this schooner because my final copy is not finished. Meanwhile I hope to learn whether or not you want to see it. Be careful. Don't ask for it unless you really want it. The publishers I send it to will *not* be the Houghton Mifflin Company. The book in its present form flabbergasts me. Perhaps it is Nga's last present to me. Perhaps, through her death, she has given me a new, youthful outlook on life, a new (unwanted) freedom that has been reflected in the book. There is none of the *Moonlight* superficiality and pseudo-sophistication in it. It is simply a happy-go-lucky idyll of atoll life, told from day to day, as things occur, with no attempt to be spectacular, or profound, or literary.

Concerning present-day Puka Puka life, you'll get your fill of it when you read the letters. I have no heart to write any more on the subject. It is enough to say that there have been no changes.

The abrupt change of mood in the second paragraph of this letter was disquieting, but it prepared me for the one that was to follow:

I am not sending the Letters manuscript either to you or to the publishers. What a pair of fools we were: you to suggest them and me to write them! I take back what I said about Mr. Greenslet. He is a man of sense and good judgment. And yet I was sore because he hadn't written me some such drivel as, "Oh, Mr. Frisbie! We're simply thrilled by your prospectus for the book of letters! We know they are going to be wonderful, and I can scarcely wait until I see the manuscript."

The letters are simply awful. Thank God I didn't have the manuscript ready to send by the last ship! You and I know, or should know, that good letters cannot be written to order. At any rate, Mr. Greenslet knew. I am not blaming you — don't think it. I am blaming myself. The woodenness, the lifelessness of the first few letters should have convinced me of the impossibility of such a task. Letters are life itself. They can't be manufactured — not even by a man who wants a boat more than anything else in the world.

When I think of some of my abortive efforts at writing, it comforts me to remember the time, back in the early twenties, when you went to Iceland to write a book for Harper's. You kept sending us idiotic poems in your letters. One steamer day Nordhoff and I and several others were sitting on the Bougainville Club veranda reading our mail. Nordhoff read us a poem you had sent him called "A Winter Evening," or some such title. It was about a meal you'd had in an Iceland farmhouse where they gave you a whole boiled sheep's head and a glass of schnapps for your supper. Nordhoff read it without cracking a smile. Then he said: "It's a bad sign when Hall gets to writing crazy verse. It means that he's in a jam and can't get on with his serious work." And I remember that you never did finish the Iceland book.

* * *

[199]

After the disillusionment and disgust caused by his failure with the book of letters, there followed a long period of silence, and when I next heard from him he said nothing about writing. The letter was all about his reactions to Nga's death and his first attempts at educating his children. His oldest boy, Charles, was living with relatives in Rarotonga. The four younger children were with him at Puka Puka.

I have learned that to preserve one's sanity it is important to forget one's wife. At first I thought I was callous in trying to do so. I reached the point where I could no longer visualize Nga's face. Then, after long yearning to dream of her, the dream came. I woke up with a keen and not at all morbid desire to commit suicide. Had it not been for the children I know that I would have walked quietly to the medicine-chest and taken morphine with infinite pleasure. That dream taught me why my brain has, mechanically, as an act of defense, blocked off thoughts of Nga; kept the widower sane by not permitting him to visualize her face. She died on January 14th and it was the night of June 23–24 that I dreamed of her. She was not dead; we were about to sail for distant parts and were obliged to leave all of our portable property behind — very evident symbolism.

After Nga's death it was supposed that I would marry again. I was expected to, not for my own sake but for that of the children. Suitable wives were pointed out to me. I was advised, encouraged, even coerced. It was believed that no man could possibly bring up four little children. I didn't agree. I failed to see why a man cannot bring up children as well as a woman, and now, after seven months' experience, I know that he can. All this "only a mother knows" is rubbish. A man is quite as capable as a woman, though usually he is too lazy to take

[200]

on the job. Often he is better equipped. He is not apt to spoil his children by sloppy sentiment. He makes them self-reliant.

Of course, I prefer to lie on the beach, smoke a pipe and meditate. But I can forego such indolent pleasure, if, otherwise, it means the boredom of a wife I do not love — a utility wife.

I am fond of toddlers, but this is not sloppy sentiment. I do not enjoy kissing them, petting them, talking to them in the so-called language of infants. I feel genuine concern over their troubles, and I watch them develop with interest and amusement. I find a certain crafty pleasure in devising methods by which they can be trained in such a way that they enjoy being trained, and at the same time I am not overfatigued. For instance, making them wash their faces and brush their hair each morning.

At first I thought this was impossible. Perhaps one hundred times I told them, ordered them, begged them to go to the bathhouse each morning to wash their faces and brush their hair. If I had been clever I would have learned, after the first forty or fifty times, that the method was faulty, but it took all these failures to teach me. Then I hit on the following plan.

Night and bedtime. We are all inside one immense mosquito-net, standing on our heads, yelling, hula-hula-ing, fighting, wrestling, and in other ways behaving like normal human beings. Suddenly I holler: "Johnny!" She turns a couple of somersaults to land on top of me. "Stand up!" I snarl. She does so. "Are you going to wash your face and comb your hair the first thing in the morning?" I ask. "Yes, Papa," she replies. "Are you going to dress yourself neatly and say, 'Good morning, Papa'?" "Yes, Papa." "Okay," I say. "Now tell me what you are going to do." Johnny replies: "In the morning I'm gonna wash my face, comb my hair, dress neatly, and say, 'Good morning, Papa.'" "Good girl," I say. "Good night, Johnny." "Good night, Papa," she says.

Then I call the next toddler, in the harsh tones he knows so well. "Hardpan Jake! Come here!"

He hops across the mat on one leg, comes stiffly to attention at my feet, and repeats what Johnny has said.

Next I call Elaine who is naturally a serious child. She goes through the speech a trifle self-consciously and timidly.

Ngatokoruaimatauea is too young to speak English correctly, but she waddles up just to be one of the gang, giggles, makes a quacking noise and returns to her section of the sleeping-mat.

Next morning all four children rise earlier than usual, so impatient are they to play the game. When they have washed their faces, combed their hair and dressed neatly, they slip noiselessly inside the mosquito-net and line up at my feet. Johnny tickles me until I wake; then in ear-splitting unison, they yell: "GOOD MORNING, PAPA!"

The lesson had to be repeated a few times, but only a few, and they have been taught other lessons in the same way. It works like a charm. I pass my method on to you, Hall-Tané, so that you can amaze Sarah and the neighbors by the ease with which you train Miss Nancy Ella. I could continue this subject for hours.

As a matter of fact, he did continue it for six more type-written pages, relating how he taught them not to cry without cause, with such success that they would not cry when the father himself thought they had ample reason to do so. He loved writing about his children as much as he loved dream-

ing about his boat. As for the customary hullabaloo that all
healthy children make, that was music to him. He ends the
letter with:

Think you a little din can daunt my ears?
Have I not in my time heard lions roar?
Have I not heard the sea, puffed up with winds,
Rage like an angry boar chaféd with sweat?

Then came World War II. I heard Mr. Chamberlain's announcement of the beginning of hostilities via the radio, at
one o'clock in the morning, Tahiti time, but it was much later
that the news reached Puka Puka. Frisbie's next letter was
dated Puka Puka, November 12th, 1940.

I hope that you are still among the living, and still on
Tahiti; that you have not succumbed to the Faustian
madness and gone to war — at your age. I am eating coconuts and fish on Puka Puka, but preparing to leave soon
for Fiji. I have read nothing about the war since the news
came that Pétain asked for an Armistice. Such news as I
do get comes from old William. "Plenty bomu-bomu in
Lonidoni," he tells me. Lonidoni is, of course, London.
William has a vague notion, at least, of what a bomb is.
He knows that it falls from the sky and makes a fearful
noise when it hits the earth. "Bomu-bomu . . . Whang!
Too much bomu-bomu in Lonidoni. Haw, haw, haw!"
I am going to Fiji in the schooner *Tagua* which is carrying lepers from Penrhyn Island to the leper colony at
Makogai, Fiji. I am losing my mind, of course, which is
the reason I will travel on a leper ship. I am not really
crazy or demented, but I am losing contact with the
Faustian culture and entering into the Magian culture of

[203]

Puka Puka. It's true. I find myself continually thinking in Puka Pukan, and it requires an effort to shift back to English. When a man thinks in a new language he enters into the culture of that language. I have discovered all this by reading the two volumes of Spengler's *Decline of the West*. I wonder if it is possible for me to live anywhere else than Puka Puka, after this long time? I'm afraid not, but I'm going to Fiji to find out.

I am taking Johnny with me, also my branch storekeeper, Araipu. Araipu has 300 pounds; I have somewhat less than 100. If we find a boat for sale cheap in Suva we will buy it. I have written to Farrar & Rinehart and to the *Atlantic Monthly* for an advance on future work — total, $2500. If they come through I will certainly buy my boat. Araipu and I will convert it into a sea-peddler. He is shrewd and tight-fisted and will make a good supercargo. I will be captain and navigator. Araipu will make money while I write of things of the spirit. We expect to take cargoes of mats to Honolulu where there is a good market for them. Mats that can be bought on Puka Puka at four cents a foot retail in Honolulu at 22½ cents a foot. We will buy trade goods with our earnings to sell on Puka Puka. It's not a grand money-making scheme, but it should keep us in beef and biscuits, and, maybe, pay for some schooling for my children, in Honolulu.

I am also taking with me a 150,000-word novel, *The Saga of Mr. Moonlight*. It has none of the faults of *Mr. Moonlight's Island*. When you receive the copy I have sent you, temper to the shorn lamb your criticism of *Mr. Moonlight's Island*. It was written while I was nursing Nga. Recollect that I was alone with her for a year and a half, most of the time on Matauea Point, and that during this time she was dying and I was trying to escape awareness of tragedy by writing. It made little difference to me what I wrote, so long as the clatter of the type-writer keys dulled for a time the sound of Nga's coughing.

Six weeks later he wrote from Suva, Fiji. Once more his hopeful plans had gone to pot. Everything had promised so well, he thought, but he'd been too optimistic. He had found a boat in Suva that would have served well for the sea-peddler business, and had taken an immediate option on it, thinking that the *Atlantic Monthly* and his publishers, Farrar & Rine-hart, would advance the money he had asked for. This, with the money that he and Araipu, his branch storekeeper, already had would have enabled him to buy the boat. But both the *Atlantic* and his publishers had turned him down. Now the option was about to expire and he would expire with it.

I suppose if I had asked for an advance to go to the war zone to report grewsome details of wholesale mur-der, I could have gotten all the cash I wanted. But I wished to write of peaceful happy days under the tropic sun, and all that would be a drug on the market.

Now our money is about gone, and we have no boat. Three of my children are on Puka Puka and God knows when I will see them again. As you have sometimes, and eloquently, said: I am bitched, bewitched, blighted and bewildered. What in particular has bewitched me has been my own foolishness. I am always too hopeful. Now I will make a confession.

He then told me that the book of letters he had written had not been destroyed as it should have been, but altered to Journal form, and now comprised *The Saga of Mr. Moon-light*. A man who wanted a boat so badly was compelled to compromise with his literary conscience. His references to

[205]

the half-million-words *Moonlight* trilogy were very confusing. In some letters he spoke of it as finished and the complete manuscript sent to his publishers. In other and later letters he was still at work on it. His titles for the three parts changed from letter to letter. I gave up trying to grasp the nature of its contents. I decided that he must have been telling the simple truth when he wrote, "The thing has gotten out of hand. Before I was halfway through I'd forgotten how it started."

Then came a long period without news. The next letter, undated, was written from Puka Puka. The unhappy Fiji experience seemed to have been forgotten, the memory of it stored away in some unused corner of his mind to gather thickening veils of cobwebs.

As the years slip by I shuffle off all the dross of mere acquaintanceship and cling to the few real friends with whom I have something in common. I had, to begin with, a measurable capacity for friendship. Now, with middle-age upon me, the few friends are fewer. I have not only more room for those who remain, but a greater capacity to appreciate them. In old age, if there is but one friend left, I hope it may be you. Please keep writing even though my letters come only at long intervals.

It seems odd that even you, after all these years, should ask why I persist in living on such a lonely island as Puka Puka, with a trading schooner coming only once or twice per year, and without (thank God!) another white man here. I seem to have known the answer for years, without even thinking of it.

Yesterday evening I was sitting on the point at Yato. My mood was contemplative; physically, I scarcely existed; spiritually, I was in harmony with my surroundings. I stared across the crescent-shaped bay to the main islet. A few houses on the far beach were white in the evening sunlight, but farther back in the groves they were scarcely visible. The deep shadows suggested sleep, as did the coconut palms. These last held their fronds silent and still, in deep dreamless sleep; but when a faint breeze passed over them, whispering some dream image, the fronds stirred slightly in their sleep, then rested once more as the image passed away.

"The dreaming palms have escaped awareness of life," I thought. I recalled that Spengler fancies man would do the same. He writes: "Man seeks to return out of the life of freedom into the vegetal servitude from which he was emancipated into individuality and loneliness." I must be trying to do this.

"I am lost, happily lost," I thought. "I am slipping so far from awareness of the world I live in that the dreaming palms are more real to me than men and women of my own blood." Then, Hall, you appeared at my side and listened courteously while I went on with my meditations, as I am doing now on paper in answer to the question, why I remain on Puka Puka.

I enjoy activities conducive to contemplation; for example, the making of sails and fish-nets. I can tie or stitch all day long, with scarcely a thought of what I am doing, but with each knot or stitch conjuring up some picture, or a series of them, that bring felicity to the mind. I travel the Arabian desert with Doughty, or, perhaps, the countryside of England. I argue with my three favorite thinkers, Bergson, Spengler, and Pareto. I enjoy in retrospect actual experiences that gave me pleasure, and still more those lived vicariously in the pages of George Borrow, De Quincey, Marcel Proust, Keats or Villon.

I am not physically lazy, but I find most recreations

distasteful. I enjoy sailing my canoe, for, although it is too exciting to allow one to slip into the contemplative mood, I enjoy the illusion of life in this canoe. For the same reason I love to build houses, but when they are finished they move from time into space, from becoming to become. Therefore I soon abandon them and build again.

At Puka Puka I can spend each afternoon in the lagoon, with water-goggles on, swimming from coral-head to coral-head, stopping to stare at peculiar growths, outlandish creatures that look like butterflies, or lead pipes, or balloons, or most anything except what they are. I like to invent sentences to describe these things — sentences that I can carry home and write down, souvenirs of these journeys into a world that seems so strange and unreal to us humans.

The same applies to walking through the groves, or to fishing beyond the reef, and even more to trolling under sail, with a light beam wind, the four miles to and from Frigate Bird Islet. In this last there is an illusion of life created, if you can call it that, by the sailing canoe. There is the mild expectancy of adventure, and ample time for my thoughts to skim along as tranquilly as the canoe itself — until a barracuda takes my hook or it is time to come about on the other tack.

At this moment I perceive that you are asleep, but I won't have it. I give you a dig with my elbow. Wake up, Hall! You wanted to know why I still live on Puka Puka. Well, I'm telling you.

Take the economic side of the question. Even when I am penniless I still eat, sleep under a roof, and have an occasional bottle of mangaro beer. My income of $50 per month corresponds to that of a millionaire in the U.S.A. I have many servants: a washerwoman — when we have soap to wash with — old Mama, my head cook, two fishermen when I am too lazy to fish for myself, two women food gatherers, two youths to climb coconut palms and throw down green drinking-nuts; to gather firewood, carry water, and paddle my canoe when the breeze fails. And, best of all, old William the Heathen, my private bard, storyteller and comedian. Of course, one person could do all this work, but why should he? I do not have to feed any of my servants save old Mama, and I do not have to clothe them or house them. Their wages come out of the five pounds per month I pay to Central Village to attend to all my wants. Moreover, here people like to work in pairs, and they are apt to sneak off somewhere to sleep if there is too much to do. The other day an old man said to me: "My work today will be sharpening my knife." He took the whole day to it, too. Suppose a secretary or a stenographer were to say to her boss, in New York: "My work today will be sharpening three pencils." She wouldn't last long, would she?

Then Ropati went on to describe the nature of the relationship that exists, or should exist, between a white man living alone on such an island as Puka Puka and the native inhabitants of the place. It explains why he was able to make such a success of it, and reveals the deep understanding he had of native character.

A white man in these islands must not go native. It is a pleasant thought to dally with in civilization, a disastrous one to put into practice. When a white man goes native, the people brand him as being no better than themselves. Now, probably, he *is* no better; but if he goes native he will not be as good, and he will soon find that the natives look down on him. Why shouldn't they?

[209]

He cannot compete with them in their own culture. He cannot catch fish as well as they; climb coconut palms, plant taro, catch a great turtle in the open sea — he can perform none of their tasks anything like as well as they do. If he tries to do these things he makes himself ridiculous. Plainly, he is inferior to the natives. But he can, by living as a white man, prove his foreign culture to be, in many ways, superior to the native culture, and this he should do. I don't mean that he should dress for dinner, sleep in a brass bed, or that he should refrain from a fishing excursion or a turtle hunt. I mean only that, in his general attitude and manner of living, he should remain true to his race.

Natives want to be proud of "their" white man, as they call an epicurean beachcomber like myself. They are disappointed if their white man does not live up to expectations. They want to admire him, brag about him, serve him in the grand manner. He must wear as good clothing as he can afford, shave often, never allow himself to get down at heel. He must demand instant obedience, within reason, and never admit himself to be in error. He will then live happily, and the natives will respect him.

On the other hand, it is of the utmost importance that a white man never ridicule the natives; never sneer at them or in any way humiliate them. If he does this he is lost. He must remember that, in the last analysis, they are not glorifying him but glorying in themselves. They elevate an erstwhile potato farmer to the status of an Eastern potentate, not because of his worth, but because he becomes a prestige symbol for them. Let this potato farmer openly despise them and the fictitious value they have given him vanishes at once. No matter how much money he may have; no matter how gorgeous his striped pyjamas or his red silk shirt, his name, thenceforth, is Mud.

I could write on in this vein until I fall asleep, but perceiving that you have, once more, I will now stop.

If all the white men who have "jumped ship" in the South Pacific during the past two hundred years — whether exploring ship, whaler, sealer, Botany Bay transport, man-of-war, cargo steamer or private yacht — could have had Frisbie's understanding of native character and his perception of their attitude toward white men, and if they could have profited by it, what a difference it would have made in the relationships between whites and Pacific Islanders, whether Polynesians, Micronesians or Melanesians.

I was in the U.S.A. with my family during most of 1940 until May 1941, when I returned to Tahiti. During this time Frisbie and I lost touch with one another. Civilian wartime mails in the Pacific were completely disorganized; letters went astray, or suspicious censors would hold them up for weeks or months. Frisbie often sprinkled Puka Puka words and expressions through his letters and the censors may have believed that these were code words conveying some sinister meaning, if only they could have discovered what it was. I received a note from Frisbie with no date but having a Rarotonga, Cook Island, postmark, which read:

I don't know why you haven't heard from me, but your note makes plain why I have not heard from you. No more excuses about not knowing where I am or whether a letter will reach me. Letters addressed to Rarotonga will always be forwarded, and if Rarotonga is cut off, address me, simply, Ropati, South Seas. I am

[211]

now so famous that mail is sure to catch up with me eventually, just as my reputation does.

It was nearly a year later that I heard from him again.

Suvarrow Island
January 15th, 1942

Glance at the top of this page! It's a fact: we're here on Suvarrow — I mean Frisbie's Island — Johnny, Jakey, Elaine, little Nga and the old man. But, alas! not with the wished-for boat. We left Puka Puka in a sea-louse called the *Taipi*, Captain Cambridge. We Puka Pukans knew nothing about Pearl Harbor; in fact, we had heard no war news of any kind during six months after that event. The *Taipi* arrived here on New Year's Day just passed. She is a forty-foot ketch that just manages to keep afloat. I brought my canoe along, and now I am here with the children living once again an idyllic life on the loveliest, loneliest atoll of the Pacific. But wherever I look I see the spirit of Nga and recall the three happy months we spent together here. I think it was Stevenson who wrote that there is no happiness to be compared to that of living out-of-doors with the woman you love. I learned the truth of that when Nga and I were here. Now I see her gentle spirit, so tangible to my own spirit, yet so intangible to the flesh.

The children are very happy. They line the fringing reef with their fish-poles and bring in whoppers. They swim in the lagoon, go hunting sea birds on the sand cays, turtle-stalking and coconut-crab hunting. A few days ago we sailed six miles across the lagoon to spend the night on one of the other islets; and the place was so lonely that, for the first time in my life, I felt a touch of panic at the extreme isolation. Today we sail to another islet five miles distant in another direction. My sailing canoe adds immensely to our happiness. It isn't the boat, of course, but it gives us the freedom of the whole Suvarrow lagoon and the misty islets threaded along the encircling reef. I wonder if we should be so carefree and happy when the faraway world is in such misery.

But the war, at least, is not so far away. Shortly after the *Taipi* had sailed we saw a distress signal at sea and went out to investigate. We found nothing, but the next morning two warplanes flew low over the island. We nearly died of amazement and fright. I don't know what their nationality was, for we hid under the thickest of the bush, only to hear the deafening roar of their engines and to catch glimpses of the terrible things not more than two hundred feet above our heads. It was as though the end of the world had come, and maybe it is the end, of the world we have known.

I am writing a grand novel, the magnum opus of Ropati-Tané. It is called *Mr. Moonlight's Journey.* I am still waiting for your comments on *Mr. Moonlight's Island.*

SUVARROW
January 30th

Work has stopped dead. This life is too healthy and natural for me to turn to artificial literary work. Maybe I could write some articles, though; they are less artificial than fiction. What do you say? Shall I write one of the journey on a leper ship to a leper colony? One on Fiji and one on Samoa? Okay; maybe I will. I would have before this if I thought I could sell them. But the *Atlantic Monthly* has turned me out. Sometimes I wonder what has happened and get to imagining things. I imagine that the "Professor" who so thoroughly disapproves of me has told Edward Weeks that "Frisbie is finished." Then, with just the right mixture of disapproval and regret, which can be so damning, he would discuss my many sins and shortcomings. The *Atlantic*, being a New England magazine, would, no doubt, shudder editorially at the thought that their one-time Puka Puka contributor had not been a model of perfect rectitude. Well, at any rate Weeks once wrote me that "there are months when the *Atlantic* cries aloud for good graphic humor such as this." Even though they don't cry aloud any longer — at least, not loud enough for me to hear — I remember that they once did. I believe I wrote you that those "emergency rations" would last me for years, if necessary.

I have my $50 pension and about ten pounds in cash. I have my four children and a servant girl to help look after them. And I've got Suvarrow. But I *haven't* got my boat. The dream has come true, all but that. After years of wanting it, working for it, scheming for it, I have come to the sad conclusion that there is only one way of getting it.

You know how government immorality has corrupted private morality everywhere in the world this past generation and longer. Consider any government you please, although France is, probably, the most corrupt of the lot: they repudiate their debts internationally as well as those owing to their own people. They make sacred promises which they have no intention of fulfilling. I firmly believe that governments everywhere are largely to blame for the deplorable state of private morality existing in the world today. When governments are such crooks, how can they expect their nationals to be models of virtue?

Well, then, I am going to abandon my private standard of morality and adopt that of a great and powerful State. As a matter of fact, I already have. I left Puka Puka owing the Burns Philp Company two hundred and forty-five

pounds, plus forty-five pounds elsewhere in Samoa. I
have to discover some balm to ease my conscience, for
it is hopeless even to think of paying those bills. I never
can. I write and write until my last spools of ribbon have
no more ink in them; then I wet them with ammonia and
get a little more use out of them. For all my good-bad
resolutions I find it difficult to put them in practice. I
find myself, in thought at least, typing this over and over
on my machine with its inkless ribbon: "Now is the time
for Javan Moonlight Frisbie to write something that will
enable him to pay his debt to the Burns Philp Company."
And I do write something, and that's all the good it
does me.

Hall, forget your own private standard of morality.
You are living in a French colony where most of the
fonctionnaires, from the Governor down, have no more
morality than so many jackals and alley cats. Take an
example from them and steal me a boat. A Government
boat; they have them I know. But one not more than
thirty-five feet over all. You have at least one unfulfilled
dream: the Adventure in Solitude. Well, fill *my* boat
with *your* provisions for the Adventure in Solitude and
sail it to Suvarrow. It's a perfect place for the adventure.
You can go to the islet I mentioned, six miles across the
lagoon, where I got panicky because of its awe-inspiring
loneliness. We'll get you settled there with all your provisions; then I'll clear out in the boat with the children
and come back to Suvarrow six months or a year later,
whatever time you want for "Solitude at its best and
purest." Will you do this? Unless you steal me a boat,
how am I ever to get one?

In a letter written a week later and received with the
above, Frisbie told me that besides himself and his children

there were six others on Suvarrow at this time: three white men who were surveying the island and three Manihiki natives they had brought along for helpers. Frisbie was taken aback by finding these intruders: what were these white men doing there, surveying *his* island? For all that, he enjoyed their company at times, and Suvarrow, with its thirty islets including bush-covered cays where thousands of seafowl nested, had room and to spare for the dozen human beings thrown together by chance.

And now, forgetting everything but the joys of the present moment; forgetting even his children, so he said, Frisbie settled down to one of his periodic bouts of uninterrupted reading. He had brought with him, among his other favorite books, Villon's *Poems,* Montaigne's *Essays* and Charles Lamb's *Letters.* What he particularly loved while reading was the contrast between his own actual surroundings and those of the author of whatever book he held in his hands. He gave such complete and absorbed attention to what he read as to lose all awareness of present time and place. Glancing up from the page, François Villon's fifteenth-century Paris, or Charles Lamb's London, would slowly fade from view and he would again find himself sitting in the shade of one of the ancient *tamanu* trees on Suvarrow, looking out over the great lagoon, and he would hear the faint cries of the sea birds and the subdued thunder of the surf along the windward reefs. "As I lay my book aside for a moment I become vaguely cognizant of present-day Suvarrow, while in spirit I am still in Lamb's London, with Manning, Coleridge, Hazlitt, George Dyer. Then I hear Johnny's voice, and Jakey's. A mingled feeling of surprise and pain comes over me: surprise because I begin to remember that I am on an islet in the South Seas; pain, because for an instant I feel that I have been neglecting my children — neglecting them since August 22nd, 1800, when Lamb's priceless letter to Manning was written. I have been neglecting them for the one hundred and forty-two years it has taken me to return to them. Perhaps they have forgotten me. Now I shall have to renew their acquaintance and coax back their friendship."

One day while reading he glanced up from his book to see a cutter "rounding the point of Turtle Islet."

> I couldn't believe my eyes. For half a minute I thought it was you coming in with the boat I'd asked you to steal for me; but as the letter I had written you was still here, that glorious conjecture had to be abandoned. I ran for my binoculars. A heavy sea was making up. When the boat rose on a crest I could see a man standing at the starboard shrouds and another at the wheel. Both, like good sailors, kept their eyes ahead, and this took courage, for every moment or two a great sea would surge up behind the little boat, lift her stern until she was all but standing on her bowsprit, fling her forward a few yards, then roll under to set her on her stern until the bowsprit was pointing to the zenith.

The boat was the *Vagus* — "the finest little vessel I've ever seen, heard of, or dreamed of." Frisbie then filled two pages with a description of the boat. John Pratt, an Englishman, was the owner. He had come from England via the West Indies and Panama, making the passage from Panama to Rarotonga in eight-odd days. Later, at lonely Palmerston Island he was joined by Ronald Powell, an old friend of Frisbie, who was to pilot him to Suvarrow and other islands of the northern Cooks.

[217]

Only a few days after the arrival of the *Vagus*, Suvarrow Island was all but destroyed by one of the worst hurricanes that ever crossed that part of the Pacific, but Frisbie and his children survived it.

* * *

Frisbie's January letters from Suvarrow and a third, written six weeks after the hurricane, reached me at the same time.

I am now in a position to say that you and Nordhoff, in your tale, *The Hurricane*, described with great fidelity to truth precisely what happens on a lagoon island struck by such a storm. I am surprised that you could have done this without, yourselves, having gone through the frightful experience. The Frisbies know, now, what it is, and so do our companions in disaster. There were thirteen of us in all. Despite the supposed unluckiness of the number no one was lost. It seems incredible, but so it is. Jimmy, one of the Manihiki natives here with the surveyors, was through the Hikueru hurricane in which nearly 500 were drowned. He says the Suvarrow hurricane was even worse.

It had been blowing great guns all day — this was February 19th — and the sea was an awe-inspiring sight. At night we thought we were in the worst of it. Half of Anchorage Islet, where we were, was flooded, and several hundred trees were down; but the wind at that time was only a zephyr. At four A.M. on the 20th the sea began sweeping completely across the land in waves no more than a foot deep, at first. I took little Nga on my back and ran with the other children to the reef-boat which we had made fast to a stump at the highest part of the island. I thought we might be able to ride the storm out in the boat, but we were no sooner in it than out of the darkness came a sea about six feet deep moving as fast as an express train. It swamped the boat and nearly capsized it. The miracle is that the children weren't drowned, it came so suddenly; any but Puka Puka kids would have been swept on into the lagoon. When the wave had passed we fought our way in pitch darkness, with the combined roar of wind and sea in our ears, to the biggest *tamanu* tree on the island. I managed to get all the children up the tree before the next sea came. I lashed the four of them to the biggest limb about twenty feet up.

Then came sea after sea, crashing across the island with incredible speed, carrying before it smaller trees and huge masses of coral torn from the reef. Our clothing was, actually, torn from our bodies. We scarcely knew when dawn came, for the wind picked up masses of green sea and threw it across the island in solid chunks. Hall, some of those seas touched our feet, and we were twenty feet up! They and the wind destroyed nineteen out of every twenty coconut palms, and all but five of the *tamanu* trees: the one we were in and four others within a few feet of us. These five stood because they were close together with their roots interlocked. But nearly every limb of the five was broken off except the huge one we were lashed to. One limb nearly eighteen inches in diameter at the butt crashed down between Elaine and Jakey; there were not four inches to spare on either side.

Well, we were in that *tamanu* tree, continually drenched and shivering with cold, from four A.M. until two in the afternoon. Then the wind shifted from northeast to north-northwest and it seemed to break the seas, for no more washed over the land. At about four o'clock we were able to climb down and start groping over the island, or what was left of it. The wind still blew at sixty or seventy miles, but it seemed only a breeze after what we'd had. We huddled in the lee of a great pile of uprooted trees and coral fragments. When night came the rain poured down, and the next day, and the next night. We had no clothing except the rags left on our bodies and nearly perished with cold. We ate raw fish the seas had washed up and we had plenty of coconuts, for in the center of the island where we lay seas coming from all directions had formed a heap of trees, coconuts, dead birds and fish. On the third day the sun came out and we saw for the first time what had happened.

Fourteen islets, one of them, Manu, being the largest on the reef, were swept completely away; there was nothing left but clean coral reef. Six islets remained but half of their land area was gone. Anchorage Islet, where we were, had been reduced to three rubbish-strewn sandbanks. We lost everything we owned except my typewriter and some paper which I had stored in the safest place I could find. Pratt's boat, the *Vagus*, is gone. Not a stick of her has been found.

At about this same time I received a letter from Captain Andy Thomson of the schooner, *Tiaré Taporo*. Captain Andy's schooner, belonging to A. B. Donald & Company, was, usually, the one that called at Puka Puka twice yearly.

> *Schr. Tiaré Taporo*
> RAROTONGA, *June 13th,* '42

DEAR HALL: —

Just a note to let you know that we arrived here May 14th. Have made a couple of trips around the Lower Group. Day after tomorrow we leave for Manihiki and

Rakahanga. You probably haven't heard from Frisbie so I'll give you the news.

Suvarrow was practically washed into the sea by a hurricane that hit it in February. Frisbie and his youngsters were there at the time. An Englishman named Pratt arrived at Suvarrow in his little yacht just before the big blow. He is now here on Rarotonga. He told me they survived by taking to the trees. There were five white men, three natives from Manihiki, and Ropati with his four children. Frisbie had built him a platform in the biggest *tamanu* tree where it was cool and breezy and a suitable place for him to write. This platform was, undoubtedly, the means of saving their lives. Pratt told me that the seas swept over the highest part of Anchorage Islet to the depth of fifteen feet. Some photographs taken by a man who reached Suvarrow shortly after the blow show the main island half washed away, all the underbrush entirely gone; nothing left but sand and gravel. The fronds of what palms were left are just rags. Seven trees down out of every ten would be a conservative estimate.

Pratt said that when dawn broke and the wind began to moderate he took stock of himself. His khaki shirt and pants were torn to tatters. Dazed and exhausted, he put his hand in the pocket of the good side of his pants and was much surprised to find there a wad of sodden American dollar-bills. His yacht and all of his belongings had disappeared. They never found a trace of the yacht.

What an experience for Frisbie and his children! It's a good thing the kids were Puka Puka born and bred. I don't believe any white children could have lived through what they did.

Frisbie decided to stay on at Suvarrow with the children! What a man! The schooner, *Tagua,* went to their relief. I sent Frisbie some canned milk, onions, potatoes, rice, etc., by the *Tagua*. He may have gone with her to Rakahanga. If so, I'll be seeing him there in about ten days.

Knowing Frisbie, my guess is that, even in the midst of all that hell, he was thinking, "I'll make some publisher pay dearly for this if I survive and get around to writing about it."

Yours

ANDY

Despite his harrowing experience, Frisbie did stay on with his children at what remained of Suvarrow for a considerable time. Because he had gone there with Nga shortly after their marriage the island was still a romantic place to him and he was now alone there with his children. And they could live without money. He had the supplies Captain Andy had sent him and there were plenty of fish, and more than enough coconuts to supply all their needs. This was the kind of adventure he loved and he was bound to get the full good of it. I received another undated letter from him written at Suvarrow after the hurricane.

DEAR HALL: —

As my friend, the anthropologist Dr. B——, would say: "Describe your material culture." I will describe Suvarrow's and the Frisbie family's, now that I've had time to look around a bit. Suvarrow's may be dealt with in a word: Bones. It is, in sober truth, the mangled skeleton of the atoll that was. Most of the land the three white men were surveying when we came here is now under the sea or in the bottom of the lagoon. But, as I've already written you, a piece of Anchorage Island remains, and here I poke about amongst the debris.

I am really glad that I lost all of my household goods. I could have salvaged some of the junk, but, except for a few of the essential things such as pots and pans, I let it lie. I feel lighter in body as well as in spirit having lost or discarded the odds and ends that weigh a man down as though they were Christian's burden. More than anything else I am glad that all my old manuscripts are lost. There must have been a million words of them — monstrous children begotten often enough when I had mistaken the heat of madness for flashes of genius. Now all of the humpbacked, pigeon-breasted, deaf, dumb, mute, blind-and-halt idiots are gone. Always there was the temptation to borrow from them. When my well-known creative genius lagged I would graft a malformed leg from one of the old children onto a new-born babe that might, otherwise, have turned into a well-formed offspring, but must now rest forever in the Museum of Monstrosities. While scrambling over the piles of rubbish where once grew Suvarrow's jungle, I would now and again spy a typewritten sheet of paper all but illegible. Stooping, I would pick it up and read, perhaps, *Ages Long Ago:* a Romance, by Robert Dean Frisbie. I would then drop the sheet with a slight feeling of regret, all but lost in a stronger feeling of danger. This paper belongs to the past. Let the past be forgotten, lest it fasten its cumbrous fingers on the future.

But, alas, your letters went with the manuscripts. I had a collection of well over a hundred of them. I used to read them over and imagine that we were together, talking as we did in the old days on your veranda at Arué, with a couple of Sarah's tall, frosted rum punches on the little table between us. I did find a small packet of letters of various years. Each of them has something special to tell me, here on Suvarrow. In one of them you wrote: "You are two men — Ropati, and Robert Dean Frisbie," and you went on to suggest that, in my writing, I suppress the R.D.F. and invite the Ropati. That advice is as good for me here on Suvarrow as it was when I was living on Moorea. You had written it after reading *Ages Long Ago.* You thought it was the best thing I had written, and — you remember? — no publisher would look at it.

I believe that I am more than two men — three or four, perhaps. But Ropati is the only one that counts. If I die before you do I want you to remember the Ropati and forget the others.

No so long ago you sent me two books, by a man named William Saroyan, and you said that some of my writing reminded you of his. Therefore I read the two books eagerly, and when I had finished them I was sick at heart. I thought: "Does Hall really see a resemblance between us?" And I replied to my own question: "Yes, because there is a resemblance." I can see it. It is not in the way we write or in what we write. But we are both preoccupied with ourselves; this must have been what you meant. I know this man's work only through the two books you sent, but it seems to me that he glories in publicizing himself. I don't. I loathe myself whenever I do it. I want you to know this about me, though you should have known it long since. I am a thwarted idealist. All my life I have longed to do fine serious work, but I haven't the gift. I do have it, I believe, for a page or two, a paragraph or two, now and then, but never for long. Despair seizes Ropati's heart; the pen drops from his fingers and Robert Dean Frisbie takes it. He says: "The hell with it! Be cheap, vulgar, anything you please, but go ahead and write."

Five weeks after the hurricane that marine ruin, the *Taipi* that brought us here, put in again. Captain Cambridge told me that when he saw what was left of Suvarrow he thought he'd have nothing to do ashore but search the rubble for our dead bodies, and bury them if they could be found. He was amazed when I said I wanted to stay on for a while with the children. The *Taipi* sailed again and here we still are. You alone of my friends will understand why I am stopping. I want to experience what J.N.H. only dreamed about: an Adventure in Solitude. On this ghost of an island the adventure is now in progress. But, of course, I have the children with me; this, I admit, makes a great difference. I have dropped their so-called formal education for the time being. Suvarrow is their grammar school. They graduated with honors from the hurricane. What do the three *R*'s matter?

Enough for now. If you want more details, wait and read them in the *Atlantic Monthly*. If Weeks doesn't accept at least a part of the manuscript I am now writing, I'll give up for all time trying to earn the money for my boat. But if I should, eventually, get it, I'll have to find another island for family headquarters. Suvarrow — I mean, Frisbie's Island — will belong in the future only to the sea birds.

Some time after this Captain Andy picked up the Frisbie family and carried them to Manihiki atoll, in the northern Cook Group. Lionel Trenn, an old friend of the three of us, was then Resident Agent on Manihiki, but shortly after Frisbie's arrival there Trenn was transferred to the island of Mangaia, in the southern Cooks. Frisbie's next letters were written from Manihiki.

FRISBIE OF DANGER ISLAND

I don't know what day of the week it is, nor what month, and I am not entirely sure of the year. However, the fishing is fine, and we had a nice fresh rain-bath this morning.

Tapuaikaha Islet is one of about five acres, three miles from Tauhunu Village, on the southwest reef. Johnny is away in Tauhunu Village and I am fretting for her return. Trenn built a house on this islet and we have taken it over since he left. It is nice and lonely. Our only neighbors are seafowl, and land crabs scuttling about in the bush, now and then stopping to poke their eyes out and wave their claws around as though they were semaphoring. The wind moans in the trees, the sea birds squawk, the land crabs click their claws, the reef combers thunder away day and night. Remember the last verse of a poem you sent me from the low island in the Tuamotus?

> These are the voices of Roatu:
> The roar of the surf on the reef;
> The wind in the fronds of the palms;
> And the shouts of the children at play.

That's how it is here. The voices of the children are those of Johnny, Jakey, Elaine and Nga.

Lord knows why I am living here except, I suppose, that as the years go by I find it more and more impossible to live among people. I am not working. I have done no work for six months and feel not the slightest desire ever to work again. I am at peace with the world and with myself, and am quite content to catch a fish, read a book, smoke my pipe, and teach my children the three *R*'s. But I'm not doing so well with the latter and this worries me. I am not as sure as I was of my competence as a teacher. I might have known that an ex-student in the Tingley Raja Yoga Academy of Point Loma, San Diego, would not have the necessary experience.

My conscience troubles me only with respect to the children, not at all with respect to the indolence of author Frisbie. I remember that there are thousands of books written every year, some of them as good, perhaps, as I could write. I was not stirred from my tranquillity even when I received a radiogram from Ober — there's a wireless station here — which read: "Weeks says Island story superb. Serializing. Ober." Now if Ober had added: "Instead of cash, *Atlantic* sending you boat exact measurements Captain Slocum's *Spray*"! ! ! ! The exclamation points tell better than words could do what the nature of my reaction would be.

Do you remember the time, in Papéari, when you were acting as secretary for Robert Keable? You had an uncreative period and were fair sick with a kind of spiritual frustration. You felt that you must write; that it was your duty to write, but you didn't have anything to write about. Being a Puritan at heart, you forced yourself to write, and, if I remember correctly, you reaped a fine harvest of rejection slips. Because I am a true Pagan I am enjoying this vegetative period immensely. I hope it lasts to the end of my days.

I greatly enjoyed the letter about your schooner voyage with Nancy to the Gambier Islands. I've no doubt that she is a swell little daughter and was a perfect traveling companion. She may be nearly as fine a daughter as my Johnny. Hall, why in heck do we write mediocre books when we can create Number-1 daughters? We don't write, primarily, to make money. Our secret hope is to perpetuate ourselves a little way into the future. Well, haven't we, with our children? Carramba! With Johnny and Nancy Ella we have achieved immortality! Why try to win a sham importance through authorship? I tell you truly, that every time my work is accepted I feel more than a charlatan — a downright cheat. When I read my work in print I blush to think that I could have foisted such tripe on the public. I believe that the only book I could produce without a sense of shame would be the one I planned to write years ago. If I bared my soul it would not be a printable book, but I would feel an honest man.

News! Johnny has just returned from Tauhunu Village! She is coming along the beach now. I'll finish this later.

This was the kind of letter I liked best to receive from Frisbie, when he was at ease and "looking inward" with a kind of amused detachment. It increased my longing to see him again in the flesh. We continually planned for meetings but something always interfered to prevent our paths from crossing. With World War II in progress the great difficulty was lack of shipping; otherwise we might have met either at Tahiti or at Rarotonga. They are only 650 miles apart and had formerly been connected with a monthly service. But after the outbreak of war they might have been on opposite sides of the Globe in so far as any means of going from one to the other was concerned. Nevertheless, we kept our friendship warm and bright as best we could by means of letters, although many of them went astray. He finished the one above quoted on the evening of the same day.

This morning I wanted only another helping of Lotii, if that is the plural. Now I am worried again. Why?

Because Johnny is back from Tauhunu Village and I am reminded that I have duties to fulfill. Because I am so fond of Johnny she makes me miserable. I know that she should be in school somewhere, and I can't send her. She is much more of a European or an American than I am. She has naturally nice ways, fine perceptions and a sense of integrity. I haven't. The other children are little savages like their dad. Jakey and I get along fine because all we care about is fishing, eating and sleeping. I don't think he cares a whoop about aesthetic things. When I am enjoying the changes of light and color on the lagoon or palm fronds glinting in the moonlight I don't mention it to Jakey. Elaine, I think, will have Johnny's capacity for becoming civilized, if ever she has a chance to learn what civilization is. Little Nga, like Jakey and Papa, will probably remain a savage.

My Johnny is nine, so your Nancy must be twelve. Hall, every year for you is one to the good. Nancy *is* catching up with you; you're not leaving her behind, alone and lost. And Conrad is now sixteen, almost a young man. You should worry! But *I* should, and do, because my children are so much younger. Of course, I am much younger than you are, but my health isn't so hot. That is one reason why your cursèd dream poem still haunts me. But Andy will soon be coming north again. The moment I see glorious old Andy's gold-toothed smile there will be nothing wrong with my health.

Captain Andy was one of the few friends that Ropati held in his heart of hearts. He was an unusual kind of South Sea schooner captain. An American by birth, he had been sailing the South Pacific since his middle teens. He had gone to sea as a boy and his formal education had been scanty. Melville said that whaling ships had been his Harvard and Yale. Copra schooners — the *Tagua*, the *Tiaré Taporo* and various others — provided Captain Andy with most of his education and well had he profited by it. He was endowed with a good mind and more than thirty years of omnivorous reading during his long sea voyages had given him a wide range of interests. But he was no mere bookworm; the reading was confined to his fair-weather voyages. He had enough and to spare of the other kind, for the so-called Pacific is often far from being that, particularly during the hurricane season. He was a superb seaman, loved and respected by his Polynesian sailors who know what first-class seamanship amounts to. It was commonly said of him, and truthfully said: "Whoever sails with Andy reaches his destination." He never lost a ship, although he has been through the worst weather the Pacific can show, including several hurricanes. But why do I speak of him in the past tense? He is still hale and hearty and still going to sea; and his stalwart sons by a Rarotongan mother have followed their father's profession.

Some time early in 1943 Ropati and his children returned with Andy from Manihiki to Rarotonga.

RAROTONGA
May 24th, 1943

The kids and I are living from hand to mouth in Rarotonga; the old man in terror of his bills and sorely distraught. Furthermore, I have just had twenty-two teeth pulled out. The money the *Atlantic* paid me for the Suvarrow story vanished in paying my debt to Ober. What a miserable trade Journalism is! If I can get the job of Resident Agent on Puka Puka, or if my application to serve in the Navy Intelligence Department is accepted, I'll never write another page for publication.

I received the copy of *Men Without Country*. It gave me the impression of having been written in haste; I thought that it might easily have been twice as long. The best part, to my mind, was the convicts' escape from Cayenne, and the description of the bombers attacking the tramp steamer.

So this is the way you carry out your firm resolve to leave the war out of your work! But what else can one write about in these days? I'm sorry to learn that your "Good-bye, Polynesia" story has been going begging, from editor to editor. As between your two tentative titles, "Good-bye, Polynesia," and "Lost Island," I prefer the latter. For it was, and is, a lost island. Cheer up! Some editor may see that this side of the war in the Pacific deserves at least a brief mention.

Old friend, I can't write any more. I am miserable in body and spirit.

In August of this year my wife and daughter, Nancy, went to California to see our son, Conrad, who was then in school near Santa Barbara. Since there was no other means of transportation Colonel James M. Quinn kindly granted them passage on a troop transport from the island of Bora Bora, in the Leeward Society Islands, about one hundred miles from Tahiti. Colonel Quinn was then in command of the U. S. Army troops occupying the base built at Bora Bora immediately after the Pearl Harbor disaster. Many transports, hospital ships, tankers, supply ships and the like called at Bora Bora on their way to and from the islands in the western Pacific. I felt lonely in my now empty house and had written Ropati about it.

RAROTONGA, *November 10th, 1943*

There are only two cures for the kind of loneliness you speak of: reunion with the family, or alcohol. I can sympathize with you. Every time I have been away from my family I have wallowed in the depths of depression. But, Hall, what fools we are! In reality we are suffering from an unacknowledged form of egotism. We imagine that our children are crying their eyes out for us, adding to their nightly prayers: "And dear Lord, please send me back to my papa!" The chances are that our children don't give us two thoughts a day, or a week. They are going to parties or picture-shows, having a wonderful time, free from the inhibiting influence of their dads. I am speaking here only of myself; no doubt it is different in your family. I am already anticipating the misery of separation from my kids in case I am given the job I've applied for in the Navy Intelligence Service. I've had no reply, but I might get it.

Just now we are living in a pretty little house in Aorangi Village, not far from Andy's place. We have no servant. Johnny and I do the cooking and the other children help with the housework. Johnny is getting to be a big girl now and she has a mind of her own. Like her dad she is restless and wants to be on the move, but the restlessness is chiefly due to the fact that there is no picture-show here. She became addicted to the vile habit of movie-going when she was with me in Fiji. I wish I'd never taken her to Suva. Imagine the effect upon the mind of a child whose life until then had been spent on Puka Puka.

Did you ever try writing a novel that you knew in advance was worthless? That is what I am doing now.

Three years later this novel, published by Doubleday, Doran & Company, appeared under the title *Amaru*. I recognized it at once as a story that Frisbie had tried to write a dozen years earlier. Either he had salvaged the old manuscript from the sodden wreckage on Suvarrow, or he remembered enough of it to do what he had resolved never to do again — "graft a malformed leg from one of the old children onto a new-born babe." The result was, as he had feared, another exhibit in the Museum of Monstrosities.

At about this time, in 1943, George Weller, an American war correspondent for the *Chicago Daily News*, arrived at Tahiti to recover from malaria and poisoned feet, contracted in the jungles of New Guinea and Bougainville Island. He had come via Rarotonga where he became acquainted with Frisbie. He gave me some disquieting news about Frisbie's health and a touching account of his relationship with his children. Johnny, he said, although only ten, was the responsible head of the family and looked after her younger brother and sisters far better than her father was able to do.

In January 1944, I followed my family to California and remained in the U.S.A. until the autumn of 1945. During this time Frisbie and I again lost touch and it was not until the end of the year that I heard from him once more.

NAVY DISPENSARY
TUTUILA, SAMOA
November 25th, 1945

Your forwarded letters came a few days ago, together with a copy of *The High Barbaree*. I have been too ill even to think of writing, but not too ill to read *The High Barbaree*. I don't know when a tale has pleased me as much and annoyed me as much. Who chlorinated the last part of this wish-fulfillment dream when Alec and Nancy are about to be married? Was it you or Nordhoff? The ceremony should have ended with the old Polynesian service, where a drop of Alec's blood is mingled with a drop of Nancy's on the piece of white tapa cloth. Why bring the parson in? I also object to the ending. You seem to have been afraid that your readers would not realize that the entire island part of the story is Alec's dream while dying. Give your readers credit for a little discernment. I think I would have ended the story in the little cove where Alec and Nancy are calling to each other in the deepening twilight; then have the island slowly vanish as the calls grow fainter until only the empty sea remains. However, there is much to be said for the ending as you have it. Probably I'm not making much sense. I'm a very ill and weak hombre.

Off and on I've been in hospital since the first of April. Three times I've been so close to death that I know what it is like to die. They have given me seven blood transfusions, and I have lost count of the plasma and dextrose. The trouble has not been definitely diagnosed. I get better, as I now am, and then without warning I become dizzy, faint, and lose as much as a gallon of blood in one hemorrhage. The only thing that worries me is the fate of my children if I die. It is appalling to think of my beloved Johnny becoming a little whore on the streets of Pago. They don't make daughters any finer than Florence Ngatokorua (Johnny) Frisbie.

Oh, for the peace and stillness of Puka Puka! This dispensary is a madhouse. Every day at noon they turn on the radio and it blares on until ten at night. And they play nothing but the awfulest tripe. I really believe that Bob Hope et al. are causing my hemorrhages. Why should one worry about atom bombs destroying civilization when civilization produces the kind of art heard over the radio, and the kind of humor that Jack Benny vomits out to the public? Oh, Hall, I gotta get out of here!

Johnny and Jakey have just returned from a voyage around the Samoan Group. They had two nights ashore at Swain's Island. Their report makes me determined to go there. I saw it for a day in 1935. Lord give me strength to make it once more.

Frisbie had come to Samoa from Manihiki, in a Navy plane, at a time when it was thought he was dying. The children followed later, also by plane, a great adventure for them. Like so many thousands of island children, the war had completely altered their way of life. Children who had never seen a ship larger than a copra schooner became suddenly familiar with great ships of war: submarines, tankers, troopships, hospital ships, to say nothing of aeroplanes. They lived as did their parents in a kind of daze, not knowing which was reality: the old changeless life in which, from birth to death, their horizons were the same circles of sea and sky, or the new life suddenly foisted upon them when so many were shunted from place to place and from island to island as the necessities of war demanded. In the case of the Frisbie children it was their father's health that demanded these changes. He was in a precarious condition throughout this year, sometimes in hospital, sometimes living in a village thirty miles from Apia. From this latter place he wrote, on March 31st, 1946:

I have been fairly well for two months. I find it possible to work for about three hours every other day. When I am strong enough it is important that I help Johnny with her book. We expect it will be finished on her birthday,

July 19th. I will then make a clean copy for her and mail it in August. So, what with being somewhat weak and my attention concentrated on transitions, chapter subjects, topic sentences, and general editing for Johnny, I have no time for work on my own. However, *Dawn Sails North* is half done, and I expect to finish it between September 1st and December 31st. Now that I am again a teetotaler I find that, even with my hours curtailed, I can do more and better work than formerly. But of course it is Johnny's book that interests me. Hall, Johnny is making the grade where I have failed as a writer. Recognition of this fact has given me a new lease on life. I mean to live on, now, to see her grow and develop. She is young, of course, only thirteen, but shows wonderful promise as a writer. Her story is the simple story of her life. In the first chapter she repeats what her mother told her of her birth in Tahiti. Then, in chapter II . . .

He went on to outline Johnny's book, chapter by chapter, and although he tried to conceal the fact, it was clear to me that the book was the father's rather than the daughter's. He had more or less convinced himself that he was only guiding Johnny, giving her a suggestion now and then. Of course she was not yet able to think in English, but that would come. Meanwhile, here she was, about to publish her first book when only thirteen years old. Her life was all before her, and starting a career of authorship so early, she would go far. If anything should happen to him, Johnny would be able to support her younger sisters by writing. If her first book were a success, and he felt that it would be, plans were already made for the second. It was to be a child's book called *Jerry, the Small Breeze*, telling of the dangerous and exciting adventures of a cat's-paw of wind, always trying to escape from the Big

Wind who would swallow him whole. In the end the Big Wind catches him, and he finds that the frightful Ogre is no more than a company of gentle little breezes like himself.

It's wonderful, planning work with and for Johnny. She takes such keen interest in it and has so many good ideas of her own. And so, you see, I am dreaming hopefully of the future because, now, it is the children's future, not mine. I have the sweetest little family on the face of the Earth, and in it, one true genius of a high order. They are visiting me now but will return to Apia this afternoon. I have them stopping with a family where they learn European manners. They go to the best of South Sea schools — Leifiifi. They are the best dressed kids in town; the best mannered and the best looking. Everyone is delighted with them. My only cause for worry is the old one — money. I am worth just twenty pounds at this writing, and I owe three hundred; and so, financially, I stand at minus 280 pounds. But I'm still alive with something better than a boat to look forward to — Johnny's future. I expect to move, shortly, to the tiny island of Manono which is between Upolu and Savaii. It is, truly, an earthly paradise in miniature.

I received one other letter from Ropati, in 1946, written from the village of Samatau, Samoa.

I am still here, living on a diet of milk and oranges which is doing me more good than all the doctors and their panaceas. They nearly killed me in Pago. Johnny is with me just now, working on her book. We don't know just where and how to end it. Maybe something will work out, like my conveniently dying to bring it to a proper climax. I have met here an English woodcut artist who is writing a book about his six-months voyage through Polynesia, to be illustrated by himself. I could have given him some pointers about where to go and what to see, but his attitude toward me is so plainly and obviously contemptuous that I have snapped into my shell like a hermit crab. He regards me as a sort of beachcomber author, wearing a tinsel halo of romance. Why is it that I haven't the personality of an author? I suppose it's because I am not respectable in the English fashion.

Enough of this. I'll hope to receive a good letter from you, by Andy, with all the news from Tahiti, particularly, news about yourself, Sarah, Nancy and Conrad. Wouldn't our children be surprised if they knew of the deep and genuine interest taken in their welfare by their fathers' old friends? Or perhaps they would think it quite natural. I haven't seen Conrad or Nancy since they were little more than babies, and you have never seen my youngest three. If only I could go to Tahiti, sit on your veranda and dispute with you the privilege as to who does the lion's share of the talking! Here I feel spiritually blighted. It is only the keen interest in Johnny's book that keeps me going. As for my own *Dawn Sails North,* it hasn't sailed yet.

Hall, we've *got* to meet once more, somewhere, somehow.

I, too, longed for this meeting. World War II had ended, but instead of the expected resumption of trade in the Pacific, steamship lines returning to their old schedules between continents, and interisland services being re-established once more, the great Mother of Oceans seemed to have expanded to what she had been in the days before Wallis and Cook and Bougainville had explored her solitudes. Personally, I liked this, although the all but complete dearth of shipping was attended by a good deal of inconvenience to people living, supposedly, in the twentieth century. I had, often, feared that the World was shrinking to the size of a withered orange, and, with the tremendous advance made in Aviation, I had expected it to shrink still more, after World War II. Just the contrary happened. There was far more shipping — in the eastern Pacific, at least — one hundred years ago, in the days of whaling ships, than there is today. As for planes, in so far as French Oceania is concerned they might never have been invented. Americans who take it for granted that all the World is air-minded should visit French Polynesia, supposing they could find a means of coming here. The Polynesians of a thousand years ago had better means of communication. Nevertheless, letters did, occasionally, and still do, reach their destinations. A letter from Frisbie, from Letogo, Samoa, and dated January 6th, 1947, reached Tahiti in May of that year. I was then in the U.S.A.

Years ago when you returned from Iceland, having failed to write the book for Harper's, you told me that a man is a fool to take money in advance for work. I have been guilty of that same foolishness. I accepted a $2000 advance from Doubleday, and not a day's peace have I known since. I am continually worried lest *Dawn Sails North* should fail to come up to scratch. For the past two months I have written virtually nothing. Now in desperation I am moving the Frisbie family back to the Cook Islands. If we can get to Mangaia, the setting for Part III of the story, I believe I can finish the damned thing, after a fashion.

Johnny's book, *Miss Ulysses of Puka Puka,* has been

with the *Atlantic Monthly* the past six weeks. I'm afraid it's a wash-out, due to the fact that Robert Dean Frisbie, mortal enemy of Ropati-Tané, did too much meddling with it.

We have been living here on a cattle ranch where there are horses to ride. There is a picture-show twice a week and a pretty good school. The kids have been very happy, but I'm a sick man, Hall-Tané. I hope to last two or three years longer for their sakes, but I think it unlikely. I have never recovered from all those hemorrhages. Six months or a year in the U.S.A. might help. I could turn myself over to the Navy doctors in Pago Pago, and since I am a "veteran" of World War I, they would be obliged to send me home. But where could I leave the children? There is no one this side of Puka Puka who could or would take care of them should I leave, or die. This is why I want to return *soon* to Rarotonga. Should I die here, Johnny's immediate fate would be ghastly. From the Cook Islands the children will at least be able to return to Nga's relatives on Puka Puka. They will lose what I have been able to give them in training and schooling, but at least they will be able to live as healthy savages. Who knows? The Puka Puka kind of savagery might be better for them than the "civilized" savagery prevailing in the world today. Certainly, they would not be living under the frightful conditions of the waifs and strays in Europe.

If only I could get my old energy back! I enclose a snapshot of myself and the four children. Aren't they a fine lot? Do you wonder that I am proud of them?

The photograph enclosed was the first that I had seen of Frisbie's children, and the first of himself since one he had sent me in 1929, when *The Book of Puka Puka* was published.

There was a woeful contrast between the Ropati of 1929 and the one of 1947; it told me far more poignantly than the letters had done what he had gone through. His hair was still thick and dark, but the face was that of a youthful old man. It was haggard and drawn, with an expression upon it of deep suffering. But in his eyes there is a look of pride as he sits in the midst of his children, with his arms around the shoulders of little Nga and Johnny. The children are sturdy, healthy, bright-faced youngsters, a family that any father might well be proud of. Jakey and Nga show more of their mother's blood, Johnny and Elaine, more of the father's. Frisbie had described them so well in his letters it seemed to me that I would have known them for his children even though he had not been sitting with them and I had come upon the photograph by chance. Johnny's face, in particular, interested me. I could well understand why she was the apple of her father's eye.

I was again in California nearly the whole of the following year. My daughter, Nancy, was married in Santa Barbara on April 5th, 1947, the day before Easter. I didn't know where Ropati was but sent an announcement of the wedding to Rarotonga. Some months later I received the following letter:

I wish I might have been there, but it's just as well that I couldn't come. What would I be doing in a church named All-Saints-by-the-Sea? As far as that goes, how did *you* manage to get in, even for the marriage of your own daughter? But I must have been there in spirit, even though I didn't know the wedding was forthcoming. Now that I have the announcement I have pictured the ceremony down to the small details. As you were walking down the middle aisle with Nancy on your arm, did you think of that other dream walk, when she was five years old? How events falsify our dreams! If only it could always be the bad ones, never the good ones!

I wish I could, somehow, give Johnny three of my years and make her seventeen. Her book will soon be published by the Macmillan Company. If it sells well maybe Johnny can stake her dad to a trip to the U. S. Six months up there would do me a lot of good, and I want Johnny to have it, to straighten out her sense of values. Lord! but I do want her to go north! It seems to me that the past fifteen years of my life have been lived solely for her. . . . She is the only interest I have in life just now, so I find little pleasure in writing about anything else. This doesn't mean that I do not love the rest of the gang. I dote on them. They mean just as much to me as Johnny as far as love goes; but from Johnny I have intellectual companionship as well.

I'll write again when I have finished *Dawn Sails North,* for good and all. It has been impossible to write letters the past two years. When I try to, a sort of blocking psychosis sets in and I am unable to think clearly. Anyway, old friend, I hope we may meet once more, this side of the Stygian Creek.

I returned to Tahiti at the end of 1947 and learned that Frisbie had been there with Captain Andy only a few weeks before. He left the following letter which he had mailed in the Papeete post office:

I came with Andy on the *Tiaré Taporo.* We both thought you were home again. I know how you will feel when you read this letter, and you can imagine how I feel, writing it. I went as near to your house as the bridge over the little stream on the west side. I sat on the parapet for half an hour, but I couldn't go into the house without you there.

Andy and I have been here for about three weeks. He couldn't wait, of course, and we learned that you and Sarah would not arrive until around New Year's.

Tahiti was like a "Lost Island" to me, after an absence of fifteen years. Of course, there were the same glorious mountains. More than likely they look no different now than they did when the Polynesians first saw them a thousand years ago. They are not even conscious of the human insects living on the fringe of lowland around the coast. I found no friendly fellow insect except good old Spies. All the rest seemed to be *fonctionnaire* insects; Papeete was crawling with them. I don't wonder that they want to get away from France, but it's hard on the Tahitians, having so many.

I walked along the waterfront. It was good to see the copra schooners and Low Island cutters moored along the sea-wall. I saw two or three tolerable small boats, but I'm no longer interested in them.

I hate to leave this note, but you'll know we've been here so I guess I'd better.

A few months later I received a letter from Captain Andy, telling me of the Tahiti visit and how Ropati had wandered aimlessly along the streets of Papeete, looking for a few old friends. "With Nordhoff, Jones and Russell dead and you not there, Ropati was like a mute at a funeral. His health is none too good, but he has been taking better care of himself lately. His eldest daughter, Johnny, has grown up to be a lovely girl. Some day I hope she'll marry a first-class fellow who will make her a good husband. She deserves the best."

Ropati's last letter was written from Rarotonga in September 1948. The greater part of it was concerned with Johnny's book which had been published earlier in the year. He then mentioned his own manuscript which he had been so long in finishing.

> After working two and a half years on *Dawn Sails North* and producing a minor *Moby Dick* — or, anyway, a book nearly as long — Doubleday compelled me to delete 250 pages and add more plot. Having advanced me money they had me by the what-you-call-'ems, and I couldn't, with honor, refuse. So, *if* you read *Dawn Sails North* — and I can't recommend it — bear in mind that it's not the book I wanted it to be.
>
> After these many years I've taken your advice and am reading Chaucer. I didn't suppose I could, but I'm surprised to find how easily I learned his archaic English. I still read Proust. Recently I finished volume VII, *The Past Recaptured.* It was my fourth re-reading of the whole work. Now I'm going to give my set to a friend and keep on with Chaucer. It looks as though I've gotten mixed up in my reading, going from the twentieth century back to the fifteenth. You know how I feel about Proust, but I have to admit that there is more health in a page of Chaucer than in the whole seven volumes of Proust; and health is what I need just now.

One day late in November 1948, I went into Papeete to do some errands. There was a crowd gathered on the waterfront. I learned that a wireless message had been received only an hour before, announcing the arrival of a U. S. Navy plane coming from Samoa, and bringing the French Inspector of Colonies to Tahiti. The plane, routed via Rarotonga, was expected at any moment. We soon sighted it, far off to the southwest. It made a beautiful "landing," so-called, in the lagoon, and the pilot boat went out to bring the passengers ashore. Among them was my old friend, George Weller of the *Chicago Daily News*. Weller, who chanced to be in Pago Pago, hearing of this special mission to Tahiti, obtained permission to make the flight.

When I had recovered a little from the surprise and pleasure of seeing him again, Weller said: "Hall, I've bad news for you. Robert Frisbie is dead." He had no details, for the plane remained at Rarotonga only long enough to refuel. He had not seen Frisbie's children, but had met my friend Lionel Trenn, whose hastily written letter George had brought.

Weller was obliged to go with the Inspector of Colonies to call upon the Governor of Tahiti. During his absence I went to the little park on the waterfront to read Trenn's letter. Frisbie had died very suddenly only ten days before. Trenn had no time to give me the details. "It's a sad blow for all of us here," he concluded, "and especially for his children. A Rarotonga woman has taken them into her home for the present. You will not be surprised to learn that Ropati died penniless and deeply in debt."

Although I had long prepared myself for such news, I found that the preparation counted for little. His last letter had been received only a month before. It was in this same park that we sat, talking, on the day of our first meeting nearly thirty years before; and by the sea wall fronting the park he had tried to dream his boat into reality. I could hear his voice saying: "She's nothing for speed but that doesn't matter. I'm in no hurry, and the important thing is I can handle her myself." Many a time during the intervening years I had seen her there, a phantom ship, waiting for him.

Now he was standing by the sea wall, no longer old, and sick, and weary, for death had transfigured him. Young Ropati, the dreamer, was ready at last to embark. He unmoored his phantom ship, drew in the varnished gangplank, hoisted sail, and steered for the passage to the open sea. He turned to give me a farewell wave of the hand. I watched the little ghost ship growing smaller and smaller as he headed west-by-north for the ghost of an island — Suvarrow; or Frisbie's Island, as he had loved to call it.